The Pendulum Swings!

Literary Reflections
of a Changing World

Jeff Massey

ARS OMNIA PRESS

ISBN-13: 978-1522708759

Ars Omnia Publishing

Visit our website at:
www.arsomnia.org

Cover Illustration: Engraving of Foucault's Pendulum in the Pantheon (Pictorial Press, 1851).

CONTENTS

FOREWORD

Times change. People change. Tastes change. Modest house frocks transform into obscene mini-skirts; gentle four-part harmonies give way to pounding punk expletives; war-mongers and racists are overcome by flower-power hippies. Although these examples may seem superficial, such outward changes in society—swings of the cultural pendulum, if you will—often reflect larger changes in political ideologies, religious beliefs, and philosophical schools. Each generation reacts to the last, and if (as the old adage goes) the apple rarely falls far from the tree, it seems that the societal apple nonetheless strives to distance itself from its roots, to declare itself as DIFFERENT (and often better) than its progenitor. Really: no one—and no culture—wants to be forever known as simply "the child of X."

And so, in an effort to better understand how the world at large often responds to itself, this book surveys a generous selection of avant-garde texts reflecting (and reflecting upon) the changing tastes and ideologies of Western culture, from the Medieval period to the present. The pendulum swings!

ACKNOWLEDGEMENTS

As with any published endeavor, there are many to thank, and so I would like to extend the following:

Three cheers to Mike Russo of Ars Omnia Press, for editing the heck out of this collection and offering a suitable dead tree venue for this collection of avant-garde literature.

Exultant fanfares and diverse alarums to Molloy alumna (and current librarian) Tabitha Ochtera (M.L.S.), for expertly navigating the choppy waters of "fair use" and "public domain" this collection sets sail upon.

Heartfelt salutations and novenas to Thomas Catania, who is sorely missed here on Earth.

Secret handshakes and subtle nods to Caitlin Breen, Graduate Assistant extraordinaire, whose research into secondary materials and glosses (next edition, I promise!) is ever invaluable and informative.

Mercis and beaucoups to my highly-esteemed medieval colleague Anne Latowsky, for her expert French translation skills and insight into Marie de France. I owe you one at the next conference, mon amie.

Arias and blessed silences to Kristin Colyer, for gestating our "little works of art" throughout the gestation of this *parvum opus*.

Golf claps and finger snaps to the Faculty Scholarship and Academic Advancement Committee of Molloy College, for their welcome financial support in this research product.

Without these folks, nothing before you exists; however, at the end of the day, any errors in this book remain my own: mea culpa.

SOME THOUGHTS ON DANTE*

I. The Medieval Image of the "Cosmos"

Dante situates his *Commedia* within a Ptolemaic Universe, wherein the Earth is the center of the universe (this is the geocentric model; the Copernican heliocentric model would not arise until the 16th century); from our fixed point in space, the other planets in our solar system radiate outward towards—eventually (beyond time and space, really)—the Fixed Stars and the Empyrean, or God-Realm. The universe, as described by Dante, was designed by God as a defense against Chaos (see Genesis 1: 2) and so God is the principle of Order.

Dante's representation in the *Commedia* also follows the principle that the Triune (three-in-one: Father, Son, Holy Spirit) God "stamped his image" on what he made, and so the universe is "triadic"—that is, unified, but divisible (for the purposes of human understanding) into "threes." The "trilogy" of the *Commedia* (three books—*Inferno*, *Purgatorio*, *Paradiso*—each composed of 33 cantos) is a literal extension of that perspective, and the layout of the three realms (Hell, Purgatory and Heaven) sustains it.

HELL
Following the Classical model—upon which many images (and mythological figures) are drawn in his poem—Dante's Hell lies underneath the earth's surface (like the Roman underworld, Tartarus). Hell—a deep depression with many concentric levels, or bolgias—was created when the angel Lucifer fell from Heaven and the Earth fled from his approach. His fall "hollowed out" a funnel that reaches to the physical center of the Earth, at the bottom of which the most fallen of all angels remains lodged forever in ice, a prisoner of his own betrayal.

PURGATORY
On the other side of the planet (in the Southern Hemisphere), Lucifer's impact presumably caused a mountain to arise (dirt has to go somewhere, right?). Atop that mountain (technically the furthest one can get from Lucifer on Earth) was the six-hour home of Adam and Eve: the Garden of Eden, an Earthly Paradise. After Christ's redemptive death, the terraces ringing this mountain constituted the Mount of Purgatory, a place of "purgation" or "cleansing" where those who had died—earnestly desiring a life with God—yet had not yet fully conformed to Christ's teachings reside until the Final Judgment.

HEAVEN

Far from the mundane world lies the Empyrean, a spherical area of space (but not space). Heaven was NOT created by Lucifer's fall, but exists eternally, a spiritual realm that is—of the three books in Dante's trilogy—poses the largest challenge to human comprehension (even as Dante affords it a geography akin to the geocentric model, with God at the center). The heavenly experience Dante describes in the poem is of redeemed souls "courteously" and "in proper order" greeting him along the way to their real home in the Empyrean; thus they "show themselves" in the "planetary heavens" whose characteristics ["virtues"] correspond to theirs. In short: it's a very nice (not) place described in language directly recalling our own solar system.

All three regions are divided into threes; when their "suburbs" (ante-hell, for example) are counted, there are Ten (3 squared plus 1) sections to each realm. Dante's math is not mere playfulness. Based on the Platonic idea that mathematical forms (numbers) were the closest we humans got to "pure form/spirit," medieval theologians and philosophers took numbers as disclosures of the divine spirit, even as they took material beings as God's signature, the Book of God's Works.

Indeed, modern scholars have further extended Dante's predilection for threes into an understanding of Dante himself: we speak of Dante the Pilgrim (the character in the poem); Dante the Poet (the self-conscious writer who sometimes seems to speak from the text); and Dante the Human (a political exile who actually lived, loved, and died in medieval Italy). It's a magic number, really.

II. The Order of Dante's Hell.

A fascination with the exotica of the afterlife (then as now) engendered horrific images of the punishments of the damned, as much in response to the Church's chastisement of sin as to a morbid fascination with mundane torment. Although he may sometimes seem perverse or cruel in his unflinching depictions of souls in torment, Dante is remarkably restrained in the *Inferno* not only for his brevity (to which the poet himself several times alludes) but also for his logic. In the *Inferno*, Order rules, and the principle of *contrapasso* (often, but somewhat inaccurately, taken to mean "the punishment fits the crime") differentiates the punishments of those languishing in Hell. So while we may chide Dante for hubristically placing his political enemies in Hell, there is a rigid logic at work here.

Order: Hell is an inverse Heaven: Paradise is an upward spiral the cen-

ter of which is the Celestial Rose and the warmth of God's love; Hell is a downward spiral plummeting toward Cocytus, the icy river of Circle Nine, where betrayers (including the fraudulent Lucifer himself) are frozen in godless, loveless ice. Paradise is revealed in gradually mounting excellence; Hell, in gradually descending decadence. Perhaps surprisingly, the hellish descent is not entirely based upon the model of the Seven Capital Sins (reflected in Cantos 5-8), but upon an Aristotelean / Ciceronian model...as adapted by Dante.

After Dante is led out of the Forest of Errors by his guide, the pagan poet Virgil, he traverses an Ante-Hell (sometimes called the Vestibule) of *uncommitted* souls and angels (the Neutrals), then meets the ferryman, Charon, and crosses the River Acheron. It is then that he enters Hell Proper.

SECTION ONE: INCONTINENCE (INCONTINENZA)

Herein lie those who could not control themselves in life. We might think of these sinners as "overly passionate"; that is, they have love, but it is misdirected love (the love of money, or possessions, or your neighbor's wife, for example, rather than the love of God).

CIRCLE 1:	Virtuous Pagans and Innocent Children	(Blameless but Unbaptized)
CIRCLE 2:	The Lustful	(Adulterers)
CIRCLE 3:	Gluttons	(Pigs)
CIRCLE 4:	The Avaricious and Prodigious	(Cheap-Asses and the Wasteful)
CIRCLE 5:	The Wrathful and The Sullen	(Haters and Seethers)

(THE GATES OF DIS)

| CIRCLE 6: | Heretics | (Non-Christians) |

SECTION TWO: VIOLENCE (MALIZIA)

Herein lie those who—beyond simply misplacing love—placed their own self-interest (EGO) above the interests of others, resulting in violence. The best we might say of these sinners is that they loved themselves too much, and thus tore apart God's order by displacing God's love with their own. (But that's being kind.)

CIRCLE 7:

First Ring:	violent against OTHERS:	murderers and robbers
Second Ring:	violent against SELF:	suicides and squanderers
Third Ring:	violent against GOD:	blasphemers and deniers

SECTION THREE: FRAUD (BESTIALITADE)

Herein lie the worst of sinners in Dante's universe, those who acted with any love or passion, but who consciously chose self-interest above all other concerns. That is, they chose to use their singular human gift of intellect (free will / intellectual choice) to betray or mislead others. Dante (both poet and pilgrim) has ZERO sympathy for these folks.

CIRCLE 8:

FRAUD SIMPLE (Malebolgia—divided into bolgias, or pouches / ditches):

First Bolge:	Panderers & Seducers	(Pimps and Players)
Second Bolge:	Flatterers	(Kiss-Asses)
Third Bolge:	Simonists	(Corrupt / Avaricious Clergy)
Fourth Bolge:	Fortunetellers	(Theresa Caputo)
Fifth Bolge:	Barrators	(Corrupt Lawyers and Politicians…)
		(…aka "Lawyers and Politicians")
Sixth Bolge:	Hypocrites	(Two-Faced Liars)
Seventh Bolge:	Thieves	("Snakes in the Grass")
Eighth Bolge:	Evil Counselors	(Damn Hubristic Intellectuals!)
Ninth Bolge:	Sowers of Discord	(False Prophets / Non-Christians)
Tenth Bolge:	Falsifiers	
	Alchemists	(False Metals)
	Impersonators	(False Identity)
	Counterfeiters	(False Coinage)
	Liars	(False Words)

CIRCLE 9:

FRAUD COMPOUND (Cocytus—divided into icy concentric circles):

First Ring (CAINA):   Traitors against their KIN
Second Ring (ANTENORA):   Traitors against their COUNTRY
Third Ring (PTOLEMEA):   Traitors against their GUESTS
Fourth Ring (JUDECCA)   Traitors against their LORD

Having traveled to the bottom-most pit of Hell, Dante and Virgil then leave the underworld via a "fissure" at the precise center of the Earth (a dark, cold point as far from God as possible) and climb back to the surface, arriving at the base of the Mount of Purgatory on the opposite side of the world. There, *Purgatorio* begins…

3. "Vision" and "Judgment" in the Comedy. Dante proposes himself as a "visionary"—a seer or prophet—who has been granted a sight of the afterlife thanks to the intercession of his beloved, Beatrice. Like many "epic" works of the Middle Ages, Dante's trilogy is heavily ALLEGORI-CAL, operating on multiple metaphoric levels simultaneously. Following common medieval use of this literary device, Dante's work can be inter-preted on FOUR allegorical levels.

LITERAL (NARRATOLOGICAL):
The first level of allegory is the "simple" narrative, the story: Dante (the faint-hearted pilgrim) is lost in the woods, meets a fellow named Virgil, travels to Hell (thanks to the permission granted by a woman named Be-atrice), witnesses the many levels of torment meted out to the dead therein, sees Lucifer, then resurfaces at the base of the Mount of Purgatory.

CHRISTOLOGICAL (TYPOLOGICAL):
The second level of allegory echoes the connections commonly made by theologians between Old Testament and New Testament events (wherein a theme or motif in Christ's life is recognized as having been presage in the Old Testament, thus doubling the power of each telling). Dante's poem similarly recapitulates the Christ narrative by following the storyline of Philippians 2: Jesus did not "grasp for equality with God" and so Dante cannot climb the "little hill" that would lead directly to God in *Inferno* I. Likewise, Jesus "humbled himself. . .obediently accepting death" and so Dante has to face his own spiritual humiliation and confront his own sin-fulness, even to the point of 'dying to himself,' sacrificing his egotism for a greater, Christ-like, selfhood.

MORAL (TROPOLOGICAL):
The third level of allegory—and the form of allegory most commonly em-ployed nowadays—is didactic: every allegory teaches the reader how to act or behave (often thanks to a trite "moral of the story" attached to the ending, as in Aesop's *Fables* or medieval Morality plays like *Everyman*). Dante's *Inferno* teaches us to fear the "wages of sin" (our eternal punish-ments will fit our earthly crimes), to be prepared to plumb the depths if we wish to rise to great heights (the trilogy constitutes an Aristotelean "com-

edy" after all), and it forces us to acknowledge the reality of sin and the complex hold sin has on all of us. Sin is the human condition; it is not just "bad things we do once in a while;" it is the stranglehold our limited nature sets on us (*Purgatorio*) to which real people can and do give permanent assent (*Inferno*). Remember, the damned souls are in Hell because they WANT an anti-God life. *Hell is a chosen state.*

PROPHETIC (ANAGOGICAL):
Finally, allegories can offer prophetic visions of the future. The *Commedia* discloses the divine design for the whole cosmos—the divinization of the all material things through the WAY OF AFFIRMATION, i.e, the determination of the searcher (the human pilgrim) to find the true value of all that is, believing in its goodness as the creation of God and the object of Christ's self-gift. In particular, LOVE, human love, discloses this design; hence the role that the ROMANCE PATTERN, the love of Dante for Beatrice, plays. Following the (Platonic) romance tradition wherein the beloved woman offers by her beauty the way to heavenly truth and virtue, Dante makes Beatrice an emblem of the Church and the sacramental (incarnational) presence of God/Christ to believers in (that is, lovers of) God/Christ. She is the concretization of Dante's (Catholic) belief that God offers salvation through (human) love.

Ultimately, what the *Inferno* proposes to tell us is that "love" (the natural hunger of all people for fulfillment) is gratified only in God. The egotistic choice of "self-love" short-circuits the true dynamic of the human soul and leads only to a twisted, distorted existence; hence the representation of the damned as often grotesque. This is not God's punishment; it is the true state of those whose "love" is ego-centered. Dante the pilgrim "sees"— and we see with him—what the self-centered really look like from the eternal (and only true) "vision" or (to use the proper philosophical term) "judgment," which is God's.

*NOTE: The above "thoughts" are deeply influenced by the lectures of Father Thomas Catania, whom I had the distinct honor of co-teaching alongside in the years before his passing. *Requiescat in pace*, Tom: I trust the view is pleasant from up there.

THE ALLITERATIVE MORTE ARTHURE
(c. 1400)

ANONYMOUS
Trans. Jeff Massey

The Alliterative Morte Arthure *is—surprise!—an ALLITERATIVE poem celebrating the "later" adventures of King Arthur, starting IN MEDIAS RES, with Arthur at the height of his heroic powers—well after his marriage to Guinevere and the gathering of chivalric knights about the Round Table—and ending (as the title implies) with his eventual death at the hands of his bastard son, Mordred. It is a relatively realistic (non-magical) ROMANCE dealing with the popular MATTER OF BRITAIN; this poem, in particular, focuses on chronicling the political and martial elements of ARTHURIANA, rather than the romantic behind-the-scenes love triangles that are the focus of many other Arthurian ROMANCES. In the* Alliterative Morte, *Arthur is a flawed but fully Christian warrior-king, out to defend (and expand) a pre-empire Britain; as the poem begins, Arthur sets off to challenge Rome itself! Along the way, he and his knights engage in various battles—including Arthur's one-on-one melee with the Giant of Mount Saint Michel (a creature who embodies all that a Christian king is not)—before home-grown betrayal recalls them to England.*

As is the case with many works in the Middle Ages, we do not know the name of the author of The Alliterative Morte Arthure *, although—as is the case with many anonymous works of the Middle Ages—it was almost certainly written (down) by a literate monk. The poem opens with a paired Christian INVOCATION and heroic TOPIC, thus immediately underscoring the interlace of religion and politics at the time:*

Now grett glorious Godd, thurgh grace of Hym seluen,
And the precyous prayere of Hys prys Modyr,
Schelde vs fro schamesdede and synfull werkes,
And gyffe vs grace to gye and gouerne vs here,
In this wrechyd werld, thorowe vertous lywynge,
That we may kayre til Hys courte, the kyngdom of Hevyne,
When oure saules schall parte and sundyre fra the body,
Ewyre to belde and to byde in blysse wyth Hym seluen;
And wysse me to werpe owte som worde at this tym
That nothyre voyde be ne vayne, bot wyrchip till Hym selvyn,
Plesande and profitabill to the popule þat them heres.

ʒe that liste has to lyth or luffes for to here
Off elders of alde tym and of theire awke dedys,
How they were lele in theire lawe and louede God Almyghty,
Herkynes me heyndly and holdys ʒow styll,
And I sall tell ʒow a tale þat trewe es and nobyll,
Off the ryeall renkys of the Rownnde Table,
That chefe ware of cheualrye and cheftans nobyll,
Bathe ware in thire werkes and wyse men of armes,
Doughty in theire doyngs and dredde ay schame,
Kynde men and courtays and couthe of courte thewes;
How they whanne wyth were wyrchippis many,
Sloughe Lucyus þe lythyre, that Lorde was of Rome,
And conqueryd that kyngryke thorowe craftys of armes;
Herkenes now hedyrwarde and herys this storye.

*The heavy ALLITERATION evident in the poem is a late medieval
"throwback" to tales of yesteryear, likely meant to evoke a sense of
nostalgia and history. Although Thomas Malory's prose* Morte Darthur
*(c. 1485) would become the "gold standard" for future NEOMEDIEVAL
Arthurian lore, the* Alliterative Morte Arthure *(which numbered among
Malory's own literary sources) remains a potent—if bloody—example
of medieval ARTHURIANA wrapped in religious DIDACTICISM and
political ETHNOCENTRISM.*

The Invocation
(lines 1-25)

Now may great, glorious God, through His self-same grace,
And the precious prayer of His praiseworthy Mother,
Shield us from shameful deeds and sinful works,
And give us the grace to guide and govern ourselves,
Here in this wretched world, through virtuous living,
So that we might go to His court, the kingdom of heaven,
When our souls shall be parted and sundered from the body,
Forever to dwell and remain with Him in bliss;
And teach me to work out some words at this time
That are neither hollow nor self-serving, but an honor to Him,
pleasing and profitable to the people who hear them.

You that long to listen or love to hear
Of the legends of old and their strange deeds,
How they loved Almighty God and were loyal to His law:
Hearken to me and—out of courtesy—hold your tongue,

And I shall tell you a tale that is true and noble,
Of the royal ranks of the Round Table!
Chivalrous leaders and noble knights,
Cautious retainers and experienced men-at-arms,
Fearless in deed and but fearful of dishonor,
Kind and courteous men, skilled in courtliness,
How they won many honors in battle,
Slew Lucius the Wicked, who was Lord of Rome,
And conquered that kingdom by their warcraft:
Hearken now here and hear their story!

[*Arthur—rightwise King of all Britain—is enjoying a feast at his court at Carlisle (essentially Camelot) when he is abruptly interrupted by a messenger from Lucius, the Emperor of Rome, who rather haughtily suggests that Arthur and his knights are his vassals. Arthur objects, of course, and counter-proposes (brags) that Lucius and all Romans are instead his vassals, then rallies his troops to go off and conquer Rome. En route, he has a dream of a Dragon fighting a Bear: the Dragon wins. Later, having crossed over into France, Arthur hears of a monster terrorizing the neighborhood, and goes off to do what puissant knights do: kick ass. It is here that we pick up our tale...*]

Arthur vs. the Giant of Mt St Michel
(lines 840-1191)

By the time they had landed and raised up their tents,
A Knight Templar arrived and quickly talked to the king:
"There is a tyrant nearby who torments your people,
A great giant from Genoa, engendered by fiends;
He has devoured more than five hundred folk,
And as many wee bairns born of free-born families.

This has been his sustenance these last seven winters,
And it pleases him so well, that sot is ne'er sated!
In the country of Constantine no family has he left
Outside the great castles (enclosed by walls)
That he has not utterly destroyed all the male children,
And carried them to his crag and devoured them utterly.
Today he has taken the Duchess of Brittany,
As she rode near Rennes with her royal knights;
He led her to the mountain where that 'lord' lays,
To lie by that lady, however long her life lasts.
We followed from afar, more than five hundred

Barons and burghers and noble bachelors,
But he clambered to the crag; she cried so loud!
I will never get over the woe of that woman.
She was the flower of all France—of five full realms—
And one of the fairest that ever was formed,
Adjudged by lords the gentlest jewel
From Genoa unto Gironne, by Jesu in heaven!
She was your wife's cousin—acknowledge it if you wish—
Born of the richest that reign on earth;
As you are rightwise king, have pity on your people
And aim to avenge those thus abused!"

"Alas," says Sir Arthur, "that I have lived so long!
Had I known of this, I would have acted sooner.
It seems unfair to me that such foulness has befallen,
That this fiend has destroyed this fair lady so!
I would have traded all of France these past fifteen winters
To have been even a furlong away from that freak
When he latched onto that lady and led her to the Mount;
I would have given my life ere she had suffered harm.
But if you would show me that crag where that keen one lays,
I would go to that place and 'chat' with him myself,
To accuse that tyrant of treason against the land,
Or call truce for a time…until it may better betide."

"Sir, do you see that foreland with two fires distant?
There the fiend lurks: fare thee hence when you like!
Upon the crest of the crag by a cold well
That encloses the cliff with shining falls,
There you may find fated [doomed] folk without number,
And more Florins, in faith, than are now left in France,
And more ill-gotten treasure gotten by that traitor
Than was in Troy, I trow, when it was won."

Then the royal king roars in pity for his people,
Goes right to his tent and rests no longer;
He writhes, he wrestles, he wrings his wrists;
No one in this world knew what he would to do.
He calls Sir Kay, who served as his cup-bearer,
And Sir Bedevere the bold, who bore his royal sword:
"See to it that you are fully armed by even-song,
On horses by those bushes, near those calm streams,
For I will pass in 'pilgrimage' secretly afterward,

During suppertime, when the lords are served,
To seek a 'saint' by yon salty streams,
Upon Mount Saint Michel, where miracles are shown."

After even-song, Sir Arthur himself
Went to his wardrobe and threw off his clothes
And armed himself in a padded vest with rich fringe;
Atop that, a leather jerkin (manufactured in Acre);
Atop that, a coat of fine scale mail;
And finally a tabard of gabardine, jagged at the edges.
He draws on his helm (the best in all Brasel)
Of burnished silver with rich borders;
The crest and diadem set perfectly
With clasps of pure gold, couched with stones;
The visor, the ventail, plated so well,
Devoid of defects, with vents of silver;
His gloves gaily gilt and engraven at the hems
With seed-pearls and jewels of glorious hues.
He straps on a broad shield and asks for his sword,
Betakes himself to a waiting bent-hoofed brown steed;
He steps to the stirrup and swings himself aloft,
Reins him in rightly and guides him well,
Spurs on the bay steed and rides to the bush
Where his knights await him, fully arrayed.

Then they rode along that rapidly running river,
Where the banks are umbered with noble boughs;
The roe and reindeer run recklessly there
Through brambles and briars to amuse themselves;
The forest was flourished with flowers full many,
With falcons and pheasants of fantastic hues;
Every fowl that flies on wing flew there,
For there on the coast caroled the cuckoo, full loud;
They gladdened themselves with all sorts of glee;
Of the nightingale's notes the noises were sweet;
They quarreled with thrushes, three hundred at once!
Such swift splashing of water and singing of birds
Might soothe the sorrows of any unsound!

Then fared forth those folks lightly on foot,
Fastening their fair steeds a fair length away;
And the king keenly commands his knights
To abide by their horses and come forth no further:

"For I will seek this 'saint' myself alone
And commune with the master who manages this mount;
Then you shall make offerings—one after the other—
Honorably, to Saint Michael, full mighty with Christ."

The king hikes up the crag, over gorges full deep,
To the crest of the cliff he climbs high aloft,
Casts up his visor and looks keenly about,
Catching the cold air to comfort himself.
Two fires he spies, flaming full high;
The furlong's fourth-measure between them he fords:
The way by the welling water he wandered alone
To learn of that warlock and wherein he dwelled.
He comes to the first fire and there he finds
A woeful weary widow wringing her wrists,
Greeting him with grisly tears at a grave
Newly marked in the mud, no more than mid-day it seemed.
He saluted that sorrowful one with soothing words
And fairly thereafter asks about the fiend.

Then the woeful woman unhappily greets him,
Fell to her knees and clapped her hands,
And said: "Careful, man, you call out too loud!
Should yon warlock hear you, he'll attack us all!
Forever cursed be the man who stole your wit,
That makes you wander here amongst wild lakes!
I warn thee, your worshipfulness: what you seek is sorrow!
Whither thou goest, warrior? You seem truly unblest!
Do you think to dismember him with your noble blade?
Were you manlier than either Wade or Wawain,
You would win no worship: I warn you beforehand.
You set off unsafely by seeking out these mountains;
Six such as you would be too little to assault him alone,
For—once you see him yourself—you will have no heart
To set off surely, so huge does he seem.
You are noble and fair and in your first flower,
But you are doomed, by my faith, and that grieves me sore!
Were fifty such as you on the field or the fair earth,
That freak would fell you at once with only one fist.
Lo! Here lies my dear duchess–today she was taken—
Interred into the earth, dead and buried deep.
He murdered this mild one ere mid-day had rung,
Without mercy on earth: I do not understand.

He raped her, defiled her, and she is left dead;
He savagely slew her and slit her to her navel.
And so, here I embalmed her and buried her thereafter.
Such sorrow for the helpless! I will never again know joy.
Of all the friends she had, none followed after her,
Save I, her foster mother of fifteen winters.
I will never get off this fore-land, nor ever try,
But fret on this field until I too am left dead."

Then Sir Arthur answered that old woman:
"I've come for the conquerer, courteous and gallant,
As…one of Arthur's noblest knights,
A messenger to this piece of shit, on behalf of the people
To commune with the master who manages this mount,
To talk with this tyrant over treasure and lands
And take truce for a time, to be better worthy."

"Yea, such words are a waste!" quoth the woman then,
"For he cares very little for both lands and nations;
He reckons nothing of rents nor of red gold,
For he would live outside the law, as he sees it,
Without permission of the prince, but as a lord in his own right.
However…he has a kirtle on, kept for himself,
That was spun in Spain by special maidens
And afterward embroidered in Greece and sewn together;
It is covered with hair, all over, entirely,
And is bordered with the beards of burly kings,
Curled and combed so that kinsmen might know
Each king by his color, in the country where hecalled home.
Here he collects the fortunes of fifteen realms,
For every Easter Eve (whenever it falls)
They send it to him truly for the sake of their people,
Securely in that season alongside certain knights.
He has asked Arthur the same for seven winters now;
Therefore he dwells here to outrage his people
Until the king of the Britons has shaved his own lips
And sent his beard to that bold one with his best men.
Unless you have brought *that* beard, go no further!
For unavoidable grief follows if you offer anything else;
For he has more treasure to take whenever he likes
Than Arthur—and any of his ancestors—ever owned!
If you have brought the beard he will be more blithe
Than if you gave him Burgundy or Great Britain itself!

But look now—for Charity's sake!—chasten thy lips
So that no words escape, whatsoever haps.
See that your present is prepared and press him but little,
For he is at his supper; he will become quickly annoyed.
If you would hold my counsel, doff your armor
And kneel in your kirtle and call him your lord.
He sups all this season on seven baby boys,
Chopped up in a chalk-white silver chafing dish,
With pickle and powder of precious spices
And mulled wines full plenteous from Portugal.
Three mournful maidens turn his foul spit
While another awaits his bedtime, to do his bidding:
Those four will be dead within four hours,
Once his filth is fulfilled upon the flesh he desires."

"Oh, I've brought the beard," quoth he, "but I think it suits me better.
Therefore I will get ready and bear it to him myself.
But, dear lady, would you tell me where that man dwells?
I will commend you, if I live, Our Lord help me!"

"Go quietly to the fire," quoth she, "that flames so high;
There that fiend fills himself: try him whenever you wish.
Yet you should hew more south, sidling a little,
For he can scent you himself from six miles distance."

He quickly sought out the source of the smoke,
Signed himself surely with certain words,
Until—sidling along—he reached the sight of that man;
How unseemly the sot sat, supping alone!
He lay leaning at length, an unsightly lounger;
The thigh of a man's limb he lifts up by the haunch;
His back and his buttocks and his broad hips
He bakes in the hell-fire: breechless he seemed.
There was cold raw meat and wretched roast flesh,
Men and beasts spitted alongside together,
A cauldron crammed full of christened children,
Some spitted like roasts…and sad maidens turned them.

Thus this comely king's heart--on account of his people--
Bleeds out of pity on the ground where he stands;
Then he took up his shield, holds back no longer,
And brandishing his broad blade by the bright hilt,
Runs right toward that creature with raging desire,

And hastily hails the hulk with these haughty words:

"Now, may God Almighty that honors us all,
Give you sorrow and grief, you sot, where you sit!
For you are the foulest freak that ever was formed,
Feeding yourself so foully! May the Fiend take your soul!
By my faith, this is unclean epicure, you churl,
Worst of all creatures, you cursed wretch!
Because you have killed these christened children,
And made martyrs of those you spitted on the moors
--Dismembered with your hands, drained of life--
I shall dish out your just desserts
Through the might of Saint Michael, master of this mount!
As for the fair lady that you left for dead
And forced into the dirt for your own filthy desire,
Prepare yourself, you son of a bitch; the Devil take your soul!
For you shall die this day through dint of my hands!"

Then the glutton gawked and glared ugly;
He grinned like a greyhound with grisly tusks;
He gaped, he groaned loud, and gave grouching looks
In anger at the good king who greeted him angrily.
His hair and his forelock were matted together
And foam flew from his face a half foot forth;
Phlegm so flecked his face and forehead,
It seemed freckled, like the flesh of a frog.
Hook-nosed like a hawk, and hoary his beard,
Hairy to the eye-holes with bushy brows;
Harsh as a hound-fish—whomsoever looked hard—
Seemed the hide of that hulk, wholly all over;
Ears he had full huge and ugly to show
With eyes horrific and fiery, forsooth;
Flat-mouthed as a fluke with flaring lips,
With flesh in his front-teeth as foul as a bear.
His beard was violent and black and reached to his breast,
Fattened like the carcass of a huge sea-cow.
All the flesh in his foul lips quivered,
Each like a wolf's head writhing out all at once.
Bull-necked and broad across the shoulders was that one,
Badger-breasted like a boar with bristles full long,
Rough arms, like an oak with wrinkled sides,
Limbs and loins full loathly, believe you me.
Shovel-footed was that skulker and bow-legged to boot,

With unshapely shanks knocking together;
Thick thighs like a devil, even thicker in the haunch,
As grossly-grown as a hog, so like a grylle he looks!
If anyone ever measured the length of that man,
From face to foot he was five fathoms long!

Then up he starts rashly on two stiff shanks,
And rapidly raises a club of raw iron;
He would have killed the king with his keen weapon,
But by the craft of Christ the churl yet failed;
Upon [Arthur's] crest and the crown—the silver clasps—
All at once his club crashed cleanly down!

The king couches his shield and covers himself fairly,
And with his burly blade beats him a blow;
He hits his foe with such full force in the face
That the burnished blade runs through his brains.
He flails his foul hands at his own visage first,
Then suddenly swipes at his face fiercely thereafter!
But the king steps aside and avoids just enough:
Had he not escaped that chop, evil would have won!
He follows up fiercely and delivers a dint
High up on the haunch with his hardened weapon,
So that he stuck the sword in at least half a foot;
The hot blood of that hulk runs onto the hilt;
Even unto the entrails he stabs into the giant,
Right through the genitals and jagged them asunder!

Then he rages and roars and lashes out rashly
Full force at Arthur…hitting nothing but earth.
Yet he scythes a sword-length swathe in the sod
So that the king nearly swoons from the strength of his strike!
Yet the swift king works with such speed,
Stabbing in with his sword so that it burst his belly.
Both the guts and the gore gushed out all at once:
The grass on the ground glistened where he stood!

Then he casts aside his club and seizes the king;
On the crest of the crag he catches him in his arms
And clasps him closely, crushing his ribs;
He holds him so hard at hand that his heart nearly bursts!
Then the mournful maidens fell to the earth,
Kneeling and crying and wringing their hands;

"Christ, comfort yon knight and keep him from care!
And never let yon fiend free him from his life!"

Yet the warlock'ss so stalwart that he tosses him under;
In wrath they writhe and wrestle together,
Weltering and wallowing within the weeds,
They tumble and turn, tearing their attire.
Untenderly they topple from the top altogether,
From the height of the hill onto the hard rock
(Arthur sometimes above and sometimes below)
Never faltering until they fall upon the flood waters;
Then Arthur—with a long dagger—keenly strikes
And drives it into the hulk right up to the hilt.
The thief in his death-throes clasps him so thoroughly
That three ribs in his side he crushes asunder!

Then Sir Kay the Keen sprints to the king
And says: "Alas! We are lost! My lord is undone,
Over-thrown by a fiend! And we are ill-happed!
Our lives will be forfeit, in faith, or fugitive forever!"

Then they heaved up his hauberk then handled thereunder
His hide and his haunches even up to his shoulders,
His flank and his flesh and his fair sides,
Both his back and his breast and his bright arms.
They were delighted that they found no flesh laid open:
And so for that journey, these gentle knights rejoiced.

"Now indeed, by my Lord," said Sir Bedevere, "it seems
He who seeks saints ought to grip them the harder,
If he wishes to haul holy corpses from their high cliffs,
Or carry forth such a churl and encase him in silver;
By Saint Michael, if ever our sovereign Lord
Suffered such a fellow in heaven, it would be a wonder!
If all saints that serve our Lord be such,
Then I shall never be no saint, by my father's soul!"

Then the bold king trades japes with Bedevere:
"Yet I indeed sought out this saint, so help me our Lord!
Now, draw forth your sword and spit him through the heart;
Be sure of this, sergeant: he has grieved me sore!
I've not fought so fierce a freak in fifteen winters;
Only in the mountains of Araby have I ever met such a one;

He was more forceful by far than any I've found.
Had my fortune not been fair, I'd have gone to my doom.
Quickly now: strike off his head and stake it thereafter!
Give it to your squire, for he has a stout horse;
Bear it to Sir Howell who suffered under him
And bid him take heart: his enemy is destroyed!
Afterward bear it to Barfleur and encase it in iron
Then set it in the barbican for all men to see.

My sword and my broad shield on the battlefield lie,
Up on the crest of the crag where we two first fought,
A club lies nearby, wrought of raw iron,
That killed many a Christian in Constantine's lands;
Go to the foreland and fetch me that weapon
And let us find our fleet where it waits upon the water.
If you like any treasure, take what you will;
If I have kirtle and club, I covet naught else."

*[And so, Kay and company retrieve Arthur's sword and shield, as well as
the giant's club and hairy kirtle. Neighboring kings gather to give Arthur
thanks, but Arthur demurs, announcing: "Thank God for this grace,
and no man else! For it was never no man's deed, but the might of God
Himself...or some miracle of His Mother, who is merciful to all!"*

*Arthur then redistributes all the giant's ill-gotten gains among the
gathered people, and commands that a church to Saint Michael be built
upon the top of the mountain to preserve the memory of the martyred
duchess.*

*Arthur thus saves the day (God willing), Christianizes a pagan location,
and sallies forth on a new adventure. Amen.]*

LE DITIE DE JEHANNE D'ARC (1429)

CHRISTINE DE PIZAN (1365-1434)
Trans. Anne Latowsky

Like King Arthur, Joan of Arc was a legendary Christian medieval national hero (albeit for France rather than England!). Unlike Arthur, Joan inarguably existed in the historical record: she was born into poverty, experienced prophetic visions, found the support of a French king-to-be, fought in battle—and won!—against the English, lost the support of a French king, was captured in battle, imprisoned, tried for heresy, recanted, abused, relapsed, retried, and then ultimately burned at the stake; she was nineteen when she died (1412-1431). A polarizing figure during the latter part of the Hundred Years' War (1337-1453) that raged between England and France, Joan defied multiple conventions, including gender, class, age, and religion. Almost as soon as the Hundred Years' War ended, she was pardoned by the pope and declared a martyr (in 1456); over the years, "The Maid of Orleans" has been declared both a Christian and a national symbol, and eventually—in the twentieth century—she was officially granted sainthood. Like Arthur, Joan's legend continues to grow over time.

Christine de Pizan chronicled Joan's heroic exploits "in real time," as it were: she wrote her Ditie in 1429, during the height of Joan's popularity and power (a scant year before Joan's capture; two before her execution). Even so, the poem is not so much historical reportage (as moderns might define history), but an artful bit of PROPAGANDA...or at least a very enthusiastic expression of religious and nationalistic ETHNOCENTRISM punctuated by optimism and poetic REVERDIE. Although Italian by birth, Christine became—by nature and necessity—a prolific Parisian writer patronized by many nobles among the court of Charles VI (the father of the Dauphin, Charles VII); she is arguably the first woman to truly earn a living as a writer in the Middle Ages. Christine wrote in a wide variety of genres, including love ballads, "mirrors for princes" (courtly advice texts), biographies, chronicles, treatises on military strategy, and epistles. Christine was exceptionally keen on hereditary monarchy—God's chosen rulers—and Le Ditie de Jehanne D'Arc *is as much an exultation of Divine Right as of Joan's particular martial prowess. Yet Christine's focus on Joan—as a woman warrior chosen by God—is part of her lifelong literary "defense of women" that finds explicit focus in her two earlier ALLEGORICAL works—*The Book of the City of Ladies *and* The Treasure of the City of Ladies *(1402 and 1405)—which responded to the general (and often specific) misogyny of popular male writers by showcasing the* *deeds of the "great women of history" (from famous rulers and martyrs to the chaste and faithful) and articulating the potential of all women to achieve "worthiness" (through self-regulation, effective communication, and open collaboration).*

Le Ditie de Jehanne D'Arc *was Christine de Pizan's last poetic work; perhaps fortunately, Christine died (in 1430) never knowing the trial and execution (in 1431) of the latest "great woman of history": Joan of Arc.*

I. I, Christine, who have wept for eleven years in an enclosed abbey, where I have dwelled since Charles, (it is a strange thing!) the son of the king, (dare I say it) hastily fled Paris, locked up here on account of treachery, suddenly begin to laugh.

II. I begin to laugh heartily, with joy, because the winter season, when I usually spend my time sadly in a cage, is ending. Now I will change my language from tears to song, for I have rediscovered the good times… having well endured my share [of suffering].

III. In the year 1429, the sun came out again. It is bringing back new good times, which we have not seen with our own eyes for a long time, during which many have lived in grief, of whom I am one. But I do not grieve for anything anymore, now that I see that which I desire.

IV. And so, the green of spring has returned from its great mourning to a new joy during the period that I have dwelled here, and the most beautiful season, which we call spring, the one, thank God, for which I have longed, when all things are renewed, has turned from dry to verdant.

V. It is because the legitimate child of the king of France, chased out, who has long suffered many great troubles, now suddenly awakens, as if at the first hour of the morning, arriving as a crowned king in great and graceful might and donning golden spurs.

VI. Now let us celebrate our king! May he be welcomed on his return! Rejoice in his noble presence; let us all, great and small, go forward—may no one be held back! Salute him joyfully, praising God, who has protected him, crying out, "Noel!" with our voices raised.

VII. But now I wish to tell of how God did all of this by His grace, and I pray to Him that he give me guidance so that I leave nothing out. May it be told everywhere, for it is worth remembering and writing down, no matter whom it may displease, in many chronicles and histories!

VIII. May the whole world hear this most marvelous of all stories! Observe whether God, in whom all grace abounds, supports what is right in the end. It is a notable thing, given the case at hand! May it be of value, then, to the disillusioned, whom Fortune has brought low.

IX. And note that people should not be shocked to find themselves wrongly hated and roundly attacked on account of misfortune. See how it is not always a matter for Fortune, who has ruined many people! For God, who punishes all wrongdoings, gives relief to those in whom hope remains.

X. Who foresaw, then, the thing to come that was beyond all imagination (which is worth noting and remembering in all lands), that France (which people were saying was destroyed) would be transformed by divine mission from an evil to a great good,

XI. by such a true miracle that, if the story were not noteworthy and evident, in both what and how, is there anyone who could believe it? The thing is well worth remembering, that God, through a tender virgin, wished then and there (this is a true story!) to bestow his grace on France.

XII. Oh what an honor to the crown of France by divine proof! For by the Grace that He bestows on it, it is clear how much He gives it his approval, and that he finds more faith in this kingdom than anywhere else, a kingdom about which I read that never (this is not news!) do the Lilies err in their faith.

XIII. And you, Charles—King of the French, the seventh of this esteemed name, who, in the past, waged such a major war, which did you hardly any good at all-- God willing, you now see your reputation raised up by the Maiden, who has conquered your enemies under your banner (now that is news!)

XIV. Not long ago, people thought that this was an impossible thing; that your country, which was being destroyed, would ever succeed. Now it visibly belongs to you, since despite those who have sought to harm you, you have regained it! It was the wise Maiden, thanks be to God, who was at work here.

XV. Thus I firmly believe that such grace would not be given to you by God, if some great solemn thing had not been ordered by Him for you, in time and space, to conclude and carry out, and that He granted you the destiny of being the leader of that great endeavor.

XVI. For the king of France must be named Charles, son of Charles, who will rule supreme over all kings. Prophecies have named him the "Flying Stag" and many a deed will be accomplished by that conqueror (God called on him for this), and, in the end, he must be emperor.

XVII. All of this is good for your soul. I pray to God that you be this person, and that He grant you, without harm to a single soul, so much more time in life that you see your children grown up, and through you and them, may there be nothing but joy in France! But in serving God, however, may you never wage war nor commit outrage there again.

XVIII. And I have hope that you will be good, righteous, a lover of justice, and will surpass all others, but that pride shall not sully your accomplishment; and that you will be gentle and well-meaning to your people, and fearful of God, who elected you as his servant (of this you now have evidence), but may you do your duty.

XIX. But how will you ever be able to adequately thank God, serve Him, and fear Him in all of your deeds, He, who in such great adversity, put you at peace, and delivered all of France from such ruin, when His saintly providence made you worthy of such a great honor?

XX. May you be praised, God on high! We are all bound to render grace unto You, who has given the time and place, whence these good things have come. With hands joined, large and small, we render Grace unto you, God in Heaven, through whom we arrived at peace and escaped the great storm.

XXI. And you, fortunate Maiden, must you be forgotten here, given that God honored you so much that you untied the cord that kept France tightly bound? Could we praise you enough since you have granted peace to this land humiliated by war?

XXII. You, Joan, born at an auspicious hour, blessed be He who created you! Maiden ordained by God in whom the Holy Spirit made shine his great grace, in whom there was and is all the generosity of great gifts, and who never refuses you any request. Who will repay you enough?

XXIII. What more can be said of anyone else or of the great deeds of long ago? Moses, in whom the abundant God instilled many graces and virtues, tirelessly led the people of God out of Egypt, by a miracle. So too have you, chosen Maiden, delivered us from evil.

XXIV. Considering who you are, a young maiden, to whom God gives the strength and power to be the champion, and she who suckles France at her breast giving peace and sweet sustenance, and subdues rebel peoples, behold a truly extraordinary thing.

XXV. For, although God performed many miracles through Joshua, conquering lands and vanquishing many, he was nonetheless a strong and powerful man. But for a woman —a simple shepherdess, no less—to be more valiant than any man ever was at Rome?   For God, that was an easy thing to do!

XXVI. But as for me, I have never heard tell of such a great wonder, for all the heroes of the past, their prowess does not measure up to that of she who seeks to kick out our enemies. But such is the work of God, who counsels her, the one in whom He placed greater courage than that of any man.

XXVII. We make so much of Gideon, who was a simple laborer. According to the story, God made him fight, and nobody could stop him; he conquered everything. But it is plain to see that never was there such a miracle as this one, no matter what He guided him to do.

XXVIII. Esther, Judith, and Deborah, who were women of great esteem and through whom God saved his people who were in great distress, and others about whom I have learned, who were heroic, there was not one, for as many miracles as she may have accomplished, who did more than this Maiden.

XXIX. By a miracle and divine orders, she was brought to the king by the angel of God, to render aid to him. This is not made up, for she has been examined by a council (a fact is proved by its effect, I conclude),

XXX. and carefully examined; before anyone wanted to believe her, she was brought before clerics and wise men to find out whether the things she was saying were true; before it was widely known that God had brought her before the king, but we have found in the history books that she was destined to do this;

XXXI. for Merlin and Sibyl and Bede, more than five hundred years ago, saw her in their minds, and wrote about her in their writings as a remedy for France's ills, and made their prophecies, saying that she would bear the standard in French wars and described how she would do it.

XXXII. And her beautiful life truly shows that she is in God's good graces; for which reason we give more credence to her deeds. For, whatever she does, she always had God on her side, whom she calls, serves, and invokes in deeds and words; nowhere does she go where her devotion wavers.

XXXIII. Oh, how clear it was at the time when the siege was laid at Orleans, where her power was first apparent! Never was a miracle more apparent, as I see it, for God helped his own people so much that the enemies did not help themselves any more than would dead dogs. There they were captured and put to death.

XXXIV. Ah! What an honor for the feminine sex! That God loves her is clear to such an extent that this entire great wretched people, by whom the entire kingdom was abandoned, is now safe and restored by a woman, which a hundred thousand men had been unable to do, and the traitors have been destroyed! Before all this, they would have hardly believed it.

XXXV. A young girl, sixteen years old, (is this not extraordinary?), for whom weapons are not heavy; thus is seems that her education is complete, so strong and tough is she. And when faced with her, enemies flee, not one remaining. She does this with many watching,

XXXVI. and after them, she goes on liberating France, recovering castles and towns. Never was there strength so great, whether at one hundred or one thousand strong! And of our valiant and capable troops, she is the leading captain. Neither Hector nor Achilles had such force! But God, who leads her, is doing all of this.

XXXVII. And you, proven men-at-arms, who execute the task, proving yourselves to be good and loyal, we must, of course make mention of good deeds (you will be praised in all nations!), and without fail we speak, above all else, of you and of your valor,

XXXVIII. you who risk blood, body, and life for what is right, in pain so great, and you dare, in the face of all perils, to set out on a great adventure. Be firm, for I swear to you that you will have glory and praise in Heaven! For whoever fights for what is right will reach paradise, I dare say.

XXXIX. So lower your horns, Englishman, for you will never have handsome prey! In France you carry out your follies! You are mated on the chessboard! You didn't think this the other day, when you seemed so dangerous. But you had yet to be on the path on which God strikes down the proud.

XL. Back then you thought that you had conquered France, and that she should remain in your possession. Things are going the other way, you perfidious bunch! You will go beat your drums elsewhere, if you do not want to experience death in the manner of your friends, whom wolves now easily devour, for the dead are lying in the ditches.

XLI. And know that thanks to her, the English will be brought down and not get up, for God, who has heard the voices of the good whom they wished to harm, wills it! The blood of those murdered, never to rise again, cries out against them. God no longer wishes to put up with it, so it is decided that he condemn them as evil.

XLII. She will bring peace to Christianity and to the Church. She will destroy the heathens whom people talk about, and the heretics with impure lives, for--just as the prophecy that predicted it stated--there will be no mercy for a place that insults the faith of God.

XLIII. She will destroy the Saracens by conquering the Holy Land. She will lead Charles there; may God protect him! Before he dies, he will make this journey. He is the one who must conquer it. There she must end her life, and both will achieve glory. There the deed will be completed.

 XLIV. Thus, she must be crowned above all other brave men of the past, for her deeds already sufficiently show that God bestows on her more prowess than on all those men we talk about. And He is not even done yet! I believe therefore that God grants her all this here down below so that there will be peace thanks to her deeds.

XLV. Thus the destruction of England is the least of her tasks, for her desire lies elsewhere; that the faith not be destroyed, since, for the English, whether they laugh or cry about it, it is all over. Soon they will be mocked. They have been conquered.

XLVI. And you, shameful rebels who are on their side, now you see that it would be better for you to do the right thing than the opposite, to become the serfs of the English. Watch out that nothing more should happen to you (for you have already suffered too much), and may you be well reminded of how this will end.

XLVII. Blind ones, do you not see that God is at work here? Whoever does not see this is truly foolish, for how else could it be that this Maiden, sent here in this form, has wrought death and destruction upon you? You do not have the strength! Do you want to fight God himself?

XLVIII. Did she not lead the king, holding him always by the hand, to his coronation? A greater feat was never accomplished even at Acre; for some people, there is plenty to contradict this. But in spite of all of them, he was received with great pomp and crowned in full view, and there he heard mass.

XLIX. Charles was crowned at Rheims in great triumph and power in the year 1429, there is no doubt, safe and sound, before many soldiers and nobles, on the 17th of July. He stayed there for about five days

L. with the young maiden. On his return through the countryside, no city, no castle, nor any village resisted. Loved or hated as he may be, and whether shocked or reassured, the inhabitants surrendered to him. Few were attacked, so fearful were they of his power.

LI. It is true that some of them in their folly think about resisting, but this is of little value, since in the end, those who oppose him will have to account for this error before God. It is all for nothing, whether they wish to admit their error or not. There is no resistance so strong that in the face of the attack of the Maiden, it would not be dead,

LII. although they have gathered a large assembly, seeking to thwart his return by attacking him by surprise. But there is no more need of the comfort of a doctor, for all of the opposition are dead and captured one by one and sent, so I have heard, to Hell or to Heaven.

LIII. I do not know whether Paris will hold out (for they are not there yet), nor whether the Maiden will wait, but if the city makes an enemy of her, I suspect that she will give it a difficult fight as she has done elsewhere. If they resist an hour, or even a half, things will go badly for them, I believe,

LIV. for he will enter there, whoever may grunt and groan about it! The Maiden promised him. Paris, do you really think Burgundy will keep him from entering? No, it will not, for it will not make itself the enemy. Nobody has the power to keep him out, and you will be overtaken, you and your conceit!

LV. O Paris, so poorly advised! Foolish, faithless inhabitants. Do you prefer to be attacked rather than make peace with your prince? Certainly your great resistance will destroy you, if you are not careful! Much better to ask for mercy by supplication. You are going about this all wrong!

LVI. I am talking about the bad ones, but there are many good ones, no doubt, who dare not speak, I believe, for whom it is doubtless a great displeasure that their prince is being rejected in this way. They will not have deserved the punishment that Paris is asking for, in which many will lose their lives.

LVII. And you, all you rebel cities and peoples who have renounced your lord, and all those men and women who have rejected him in favor of the other one, now may it be all smoothed over by gentleness and seeking of forgiveness! For if you are taken by force, you will come into this gift too late.

LVIII. He holds off as much as possible so that there may be no killing nor cuts to human flesh, for he is pained by bloodshed. But to the strong one who does not wish to hand over with grace and gentleness what is belongs to him, then by force and bloodshed, he will rightly take back what is his.

LIX. Alas! He is so noble that he wishes to pardon each and every one! And it is the Maiden, who serves God, who makes him do it! Now please align your hearts with him and offer yourselves to him as loyal French people! And when you hear him speak, no one will criticize you.

LX. Thus I pray to God that he encourage you to do it this way, so that the cruel storm of these wars will be erased and your life will be lived in peace under your greatest leader, such that you never offend him and that he be a good lord to you. Amen.

LXI. This poem is given by Christine, in the abovementioned year 1429, on the last day of the month of July. But I understand that some will disapprove of what it says, for a person of bowed head and heavy eyes cannot not see the light.

And so a lovely poem written by Christine comes to an end.

THE MINI-TRAGEDY OF HAMLET, PRINCE OF DENMARK

(an ironical synopsis; see sections following each * for actual lines)

JEFF MASSEY (1967-20??)

ACT I:

Scene 1	G-G-G-G-GHOST!
Scene 2	Claudius: Nephew, I married yo mama.
	*Hamlet: Ewww.
Scene 3	Laertes: I like Hamlet too, sis, but he's a prince, so watch yourself while I'm gone.
	Ophelia: Oh, what's the worst that could happen?
Scene 4	Hamlet's BFF, Horatio, tells him that his father's ghost has been wandering about.
Scene 5	Hamlet Sr.: Son, your uncle Claudius killed me. Grant me revenge!!! Hamlet Jr.: G-g-g-g-ghost!

ACT II:

Scene 1	Ophelia tells her dad, Polonius, that a half-dressed half-mad Hamlet accosted her.
	Polonius figures it's because Hamlet is horny for his daughter, and goes to tell Claudius. Perv.
Scene 2	Claudius hires Rosencrantz and Guildenstern to glean what "afflicts" Hamlet's mood.
	Polonius arrives afterwards to tell Claudius that Hamlet is simply lovestruck.
	*R&G attempt to interview Hamlet: he verbally spars (flyting!) with them, acting loco.
	Hamlet then sees a traveling theatre troupe (metatheatre!) and decides to use them to "catch the conscience of the king" by staging a play. This is revenge?

ACT III:

Scene 1	*Hamlet voices his (and Renaissance) self-doubt in his

"To be or not to be" soliloquy.

He then tells a now-flirty Ophelia "get thee to a nunnery."

Scene 2 — The traveling troupe enact "Mousetrap" ("The Murder of Gonzago"), a rather clever play-within-a-play (remember, we're watching actors on stage watching actors on stage!)

Claudius loses it in public, thus confirming his guilt to Hamlet.

Scene 3 — Claudius gives a 'too doomed to repent' soliloquy similar to that in Faustus. Hamlet sneaks up on the defenseless king, but can't pull the trigger.

Scene 4 — Hamlet and his mom (Gertrude) have an awkward talk about o'er hasty marriages and betrayal, during which Hamlet stabs an eavesdropping Polonius (hidden behind an arras, the rat!).

ACT IV:

Scene 1 — Gertrude tells Claudius that Hamlet is cray-cray.

Claudius plans to exile Hamlet to England.

Scene 2 — The hapless R&G get verbally schooled by a witty Hamlet again.

Scene 3 — Claudius sends Hamlet to England along with R&G, who carry a letter instructing the King of England to "kill Hamlet" upon their arrival.

Scene 4 — Reminder: Fortinbras of Norway is a fine fellow, although a potential enemy of Denmark.

Scene 5 — Ophelia—driven mad by her boyfriend's murder of her father—upsets the court with her proto-gothic love/ death song stylings. She exits for the last time. :(

FYI: Laertes is back, bent on revenge. Claudius manipulates the boy's grief/anger.

Scene 6 — Pirates—yes, PIRATES!—accidentally save Hamlet by hijacking his boat. Hamlet also alters the letter R&G are carrying to say "kill bearer" rather than "kill Hamlet."

FYI: Hamlet is back, bent on revenge (?).

Scene 7 — Claudius plots to poison Hamlet during his upcoming fencing match with Laertes.

Gertrude: Your sister's drown'd, Laertes…drown'd, drown'd. :(

ACT V:

Scene 1   Time for gothic comedy! Two gravediggers make
           tasteless jokes over Ophelia's open grave.
           *Hamlet and Horatio arrive; Hamlet ruminates upon a
           skull (Yorick) he once knew.
Scene 2   A foppish courtier, Osric, shows up to remind Hamlet of
           his duel, and is duly mocked.
           *Hamlet and Laertes fence in front of the entire court.
           Hamlet scores a "palpable hit."
           Claudius tries to get Hamlet to drink poisoned wine
           (refreshing!) but is refused.
           Hamlet hits again. In celebration, Gertrude drinks the
           poisoned cup. (Uh-oh…)
           Laertes then strikes Hamlet with the poisoned foil.
           After a tussle, Hamlet strikes Laertes with the same
           poisoned foil.
           The Queen falls dead. Laertes falls dead.
           The king's plot revealed, Hamlet forces Claudius to
           drink of the poisoned cup.
           Claudius falls dead.
           Hamlet—after a brief adieu—falls dead. Then
           Fortinbras shows up.
           Oh, FYI: "Rosencrantz and Guildenstern are dead."

THE TRAGEDY OF HAMLET, PRINCE OF DENMARK (c. 1600)
(four soliloquies, a dialogue, and a major spoiler alert)

WILLIAM SHAKESPEARE (1564-1616)

HAMLET   (act I scene ii)

Hamlet:
O, that this too too solid flesh would melt,
Thaw and resolve itself into a dew!
Or that the Everlasting had not fix'd
His canon 'gainst self-slaughter! O God! God!
How weary, stale, flat and unprofitable,
Seem to me all the uses of this world!
Fie on't! ah fie! 'tis an unweeded garden,
That grows to seed; things rank and gross in nature
Possess it merely. That it should come to this!
But two months dead: nay, not so much, not two:
So excellent a king; that was, to this,
Hyperion to a satyr; so loving to my mother
That he might not beteem the winds of heaven
Visit her face too roughly. Heaven and earth!
Must I remember? why, she would hang on him,
As if increase of appetite had grown
By what it fed on: and yet, within a month—
Let me not think on't—Frailty, thy name is woman!—
A little month, or ere those shoes were old
With which she follow'd my poor father's body,
Like Niobe, all tears:—why she, even she—
O, God! a beast, that wants discourse of reason,
Would have mourn'd longer—married with my uncle,
My father's brother, but no more like my father
Than I to Hercules: within a month:
Ere yet the salt of most unrighteous tears
Had left the flushing in her galled eyes,
She married. O, most wicked speed, to post
With such dexterity to incestuous sheets!

It is not nor it cannot come to good:
But break, my heart; for I must hold my tongue.

HAMLET (act II scene ii)

Hamlet:
I will tell you why; so shall my anticipation prevent your discovery, and
your secrecy to the king and queen moult no feather. I have of late—but
wherefore I know not—lost all my mirth, forgone all custom of exercises;
and indeed it goes so heavily with my disposition that this goodly frame,
the earth, seems to me a sterile promontory, this most excellent canopy,
the air, look you, this brave o'erhanging firmament, this majestical roof
fretted with golden fire, why, it appears no other thing to me than a foul
and pestilent congregation of vapors. What a piece of work is a man!
How noble in reason, how infinite in faculties, in form and moving how
express and admirable, in action how like an angel, in apprehension how
like a god! The beauty of the world, the paragon of animals! And yet,
to me, what is this quintessence of dust? Man delights not me—no, nor
woman neither, though by your smiling you seem to say so.

HAMLET (act III scene i)

Hamlet:
To be, or not to be: that is the question:
  Whether 'tis nobler in the mind to suffer
  The slings and arrows of outrageous fortune,
  Or to take arms against a sea of troubles,
  And by opposing end them? To die, to sleep—
  No more—and by a sleep to say we end
  The heart-ache and the thousand natural shocks
  That flesh is heir to, 'tis a consummation
  Devoutly to be wish'd. To die, to sleep;
  To sleep: perchance to dream: ay, there's the rub;
  For in that sleep of death what dreams may come
  When we have shuffled off this mortal coil,
  Must give us pause: there's the respect
  That makes calamity of so long life;
  For who would bear the whips and scorns of time,
  The oppressor's wrong, the proud man's contumely,
  The pangs of despised love, the law's delay,

The insolence of office and the spurns
That patient merit of the unworthy takes,
When he himself might his quietus make
With a bare bodkin? Who would fardels bear,
To grunt and sweat under a weary life,
But that the dread of something after death,
The undiscover'd country from whose bourn
No traveller returns, puzzles the will
And makes us rather bear those ills we have
Than fly to others that we know not of?
Thus conscience does make cowards of us all;
And thus the native hue of resolution
Is sicklied o'er with the pale cast of thought,
And enterprises of great pitch and moment
With this regard their currents turn awry,
And lose the name of action.—Soft you now,
The fair Ophelia! Nymph, in thy orisons
Be all my sins remember'd.

HAMLET (act IV scene iv)

Hamlet:
How all occasions do inform against me
And spur my dull revenge! What is a man,
If his chief good and market of his time
Be but to sleep and feed? a beast, no more.
Sure he that made us with such large discourse,
Looking before and after, gave us not
That capability and godlike reason
To fust in us unus'd. Now, whether it be
Bestial oblivion, or some craven scruple
Of thinking too precisely on the event,—
A thought which, quarter'd, hath but one part wisdom
And ever three parts coward,—I do not know
Why yet I live to say 'This thing's to do;'
Sith I have cause, and will, and strength, and means
To do't. Examples, gross as earth, exhort me:
Witness this army, of such mass and charge,
Led by a delicate and tender prince;
Whose spirit, with divine ambition puff'd,
Makes mouths at the invisible event;

Exposing what is mortal and unsure
To all that fortune, death, and danger dare,
Even for an egg-shell. Rightly to be great
Is not to stir without great argument,
But greatly to find quarrel in a straw
When honour's at the stake. How stand I, then,
That have a father kill'd, a mother stain'd,
Excitements of my reason and my blood,
And let all sleep? while, to my shame, I see
The imminent death of twenty thousand men
That, for a fantasy and trick of fame,
Go to their graves like beds; fight for a plot
Whereon the numbers cannot try the cause,
Which is not tomb enough and continent
To hide the slain?—O, from this time forth,
My thoughts be bloody, or be nothing worth!

HAMLET (act V scene i)

Hamlet:	Alas, poor Yorick!—I knew him, Horatio; a fellow of infinite jest, of most excellent fancy: he hath borne me on his back a thousand times; and now, how abhorred in my imagination it is! my gorge rises at it. Here hung those lips that I have kiss'd I know not how oft. Where be your gibes now? your gambols? your songs? your flashes of merriment, that were wont to set the table on a roar? Not one now, to mock your own grinning? quite chap-fallen? Now, get you to my lady's chamber, and tell her, let her paint an inch thick, to this favour she must come; make her laugh at that.—Pr'ythee, Horatio, tell me one thing.
Horatio:	What's that, my lord?
Hamlet:	Dost thou think Alexander looked o' this fashion i' the earth?
Horatio:	E'en so.
Hamlet:	And smelt so? Pah!
Horatio:	E'en so, my Lord.
Hamlet:	To what baseluses we may return, Horatio! Why may not imagination trace the noble dust of Alexander till he find it stopping a bung-hole?
Horatio:	'Twere to consider too curiously to consider so.

Hamlet: No, faith, not a jot; but to follow him thither with
modesty enough, and likelihood to lead it: as thus:
Alexander died, Alexander was buried, Alexander
returneth into dust; the dust is earth; of earth we make
loam; and why of that loam whereto he was converted
might they not stop a beer-barrel?
Imperious Caesar, dead and turn'd to clay,
Might stop a hole to keep the wind away.
O, that that earth which kept the world in awe
Should patch a wall to expel the winter's flaw!
But soft! but soft! aside! here comes the king:

HAMLET (act V scene ii)

King: Come, Hamlet, come, and take this hand from me.
Hamlet: Give me your pardon, sir: I have done you wrong:
But pardon't, as you are a gentleman.
This presence knows, and you must needs have heard,
How I am punish'd with sore distraction.
What I have done
That might your nature, honour, and exception
Roughly awake, I here proclaim was madness.
Was't Hamlet wrong'd Laertes? Never Hamlet:
If Hamlet from himself be ta'en away,
And when he's not himself does wrong Laertes,
Then Hamlet does it not, Hamlet denies it.
Who does it, then? His madness: if't be so,
Hamlet is of the faction that is wrong'd;
His madness is poor Hamlet's enemy.
Sir, in this audience,
Let my disclaiming from a purpos'd evil
Free me so far in your most generous thoughts
That I have shot my arrow o'er the house
And hurt my brother.
Laertes: I am satisfied in nature,
Whose motive, in this case, should stir me most
To my revenge. But in my terms of honour
I stand aloof; and will no reconcilement
Till by some elder masters of known honour
I have a voice and precedent of peace
To keep my name ungor'd. But till that time

	I do receive your offer'd love like love,
	And will not wrong it.
Hamlet:	I embrace it freely;
	And will this brother's wager frankly play.—
	Give us the foils; come on.
Laertes:	Come, one for me.
Hamlet:	I'll be your foil, Laertes; in mine ignorance
	Your skill shall, like a star in the darkest night,
	Stick fiery off indeed.
Laertes:	You mock me, sir.
Hamlet:	No, by this hand.
King:	Give them the foils, young Osric. Cousin Hamlet,
	You know the wager?
Hamlet:	Very well, my lord;
	Your grace has laid the odds o' the weaker side.
King:	I do not fear it; I have seen you both;
	But since he's better'd, we have therefore odds.
Laertes:	This is too heavy, let me see another.
Hamlet:	This likes me well. These foils have all a length?
Osric:	Ay, my good lord.
King:	Set me the stoups of wine upon that table,—
	If Hamlet give the first or second hit,
	Or quit in answer of the third exchange,
	Let all the battlements their ordnance fire;
	The king shall drink to Hamlet's better breath;
	And in the cup an union shall he throw,
	Richer than that which four successive kings
	In Denmark's crown have worn. Give me the cups;
	And let the kettle to the trumpet speak,
	The trumpet to the cannoneer without,
	The cannons to the heavens, the heavens to earth,
	'Now the king drinks to Hamlet.'—Come, begin:—
	And you, the judges, bear a wary eye.
Hamlet:	Come on, sir.
Laertes:	Come, my lord.
Hamlet:	One.
Laertes:	No.
Hamlet:	Judgment!
Osric:	A hit, a very palpable hit.
Laertes:	Well;—again.
King:	Stay, give me drink.—Hamlet, this pearl is thine;
	Here's to thy health.—

	Give him the cup.
Hamlet:	I'll play this bout first; set it by awhile.—
	Come. Another hit; what say you?
Laertes:	A touch, a touch, I do confess.
King:	Our son shall win.
Queen:	He's fat, and scant of breath.—
	Here, Hamlet, take my napkin, rub thy brows:
	The queen carouses to thy fortune, Hamlet.
Hamlet:	Good madam!
King:	Gertrude, do not drink.
Queen:	I will, my lord; I pray you pardon me.
King:	It is the poison'd cup; it is too late.
Hamlet:	I dare not drink yet, madam; by-and-by.
Queen:	Come, let me wipe thy face.
Laertes:	My lord, I'll hit him now.
King:	I do not think't.
Laertes:	And yet 'tis almost 'gainst my conscience.
Hamlet:	Come, for the third, Laertes: you but dally;
	I pray you pass with your best violence:
	I am afeard you make a wanton of me.
Laertes:	Say you so? come on.
Osric:	Nothing, neither way.
Laertes:	Have at you now!
King:	Part them; they are incens'd.
Hamlet:	Nay, come again!
Osric:	Look to the queen there, ho!
Horatio:	They bleed on both sides.—How is it, my lord?
Osric:	How is't, Laertes?
Laertes:	Why, as a woodcock to my own springe, Osric;
	I am justly kill'd with mine own treachery.
Hamlet:	How does the Queen?
King:	She swoons to see them bleed.
Queen:	No, no! the drink, the drink!—O my dear Hamlet!—
	The drink, the drink!—I am poison'd.
Hamlet:	O villany!—Ho! let the door be lock'd:
	Treachery! seek it out.
Laertes:	It is here, Hamlet: Hamlet, thou art slain;
	No medicine in the world can do thee good;
	In thee there is not half an hour of life;
	The treacherous instrument is in thy hand,
	Unbated and envenom'd: the foul practice
	Hath turn'd itself on me; lo, here I lie,

	Never to rise again: thy mother's poison'd:
	I can no more:—the king, the king's to blame.
Hamlet:	The point envenom'd too!—
	Then, venom, to thy work.
Osric & Lords:	Treason! treason!
King:	O, yet defend me, friends! I am but hurt.
Hamlet:	Here, thou incestuous, murderous, damned Dane,
	Drink off this potion.—Is thy union here?
	Follow my mother.
Laertes:	He is justly serv'd;
	It is a poison temper'd by himself.—
	Exchange forgiveness with me, noble Hamlet:
	Mine and my father's death come not upon thee,
	Nor thine on me!
Hamlet:	Heaven make thee free of it! I follow thee.—
	I am dead, Horatio.—Wretched queen, adieu!—
	You that look pale and tremble at this chance,
	That are but mutes or audience to this act,
	Had I but time,—as this fell sergeant, death,
	Is strict in his arrest,—O, I could tell you,—
	But let it be.—Horatio, I am dead;
	Thou liv'st; report me and my cause aright
	To the unsatisfied.
Horatio:	Never believe it:
	I am more an antique Roman than a Dane.—
	Here's yet some liquor left.
Hamlet:	As thou'rt a man,
	Give me the cup; let go; by heaven, I'll have't.—
	O good Horatio, what a wounded name,
	Things standing thus unknown, shall live behind me!
	If thou didst ever hold me in thy heart,
	Absent thee from felicity awhile,
	And in this harsh world draw thy breath in pain,
	To tell my story.—
	What warlike noise is this?
Osric:	Young Fortinbras, with conquest come from Poland,
	To the ambassadors of England gives
	This warlike volley.
Hamlet:	O, I die, Horatio;
	The potent poison quite o'er-crows my spirit:
	I cannot live to hear the news from England;
	But I do prophesy the election lights

On Fortinbras he has my dying voice;
So tell him, with the occurrents, more and less,
Which have solicited.—the rest is silence.

Horatio: Now cracks a noble heart.—Good night, sweet prince,
And flights of angels sing thee to thy rest!
Why does the drum come hither?

[Enter FORTINBRAS and retinue.]

Fortinbras: Where is this sight?

Horatio: What is it you will see?
If aught of woe or wonder, cease your search.

Fortinbras: This quarry cries on havoc.—O proud death,
What feast is toward in thine eternal cell,
That thou so many princes at a shot
So bloodily hast struck?

1st Ambassador: The sight is dismal;
And our affairs from England come too late:
The ears are senseless that should give us hearing,
To tell him his commandment is fulfill'd
That Rosencrantz and Guildenstern are dead:
Where should we have our thanks?

Horatio: Not from his mouth,
Had it the ability of life to thank you:
He never gave commandment for their death.
But since, so jump upon this bloody question,
You from the Polack wars, and you from England,
Are here arriv'd, give order that these bodies
High on a stage be placed to the view;
And let me speak to the yet unknowing world
How these things came about: so shall you hear
Of carnal, bloody and unnatural acts;
Of accidental judgments, casual slaughters;
Of deaths put on by cunning and forc'd cause;
And, in this upshot, purposes mistook
Fall'n on the inventors' heads: all this can I
Truly deliver.

Fortinbras: Let us haste to hear it,
And call the noblest to the audience.
For me, with sorrow I embrace my fortune:
I have some rights of memory in this kingdom,
Which now, to claim my vantage doth invite me.

Horatio: Of that I shall have also cause to speak,
And from his mouth whose voice will draw on more:
But let this same be presently perform'd,
Even while men's minds are wild: lest more mischance
On plots and errors happen.

Fortinbras: Let four captains
Bear Hamlet like a soldier to the stage;
For he was likely, had he been put on,
To have prov'd most royally: and, for his passage,
The soldiers' music and the rites of war
Speak loudly for him.—
Take up the bodies.—Such a sight as this
Becomes the field, but here shows much amiss.
Go, bid the soldiers shoot.

A BRIEF BREAKDOWN OF THE BLAZING WORLD

SIR J. MASSEY, ESQ.

INTRO: Raptus (male sailor) and Escape (Divine Providence via portal @ N. Pole)

PART I:

Section I: Intro to anthropomorphic ani-men and multi-colored humans (but one language)
Intro future science (air cannons, link-ships) and natural wealth (jewels aplenty)
Female empowerment (lady made Empress of world) = **UTOPIA**

Section II: Various ani-men assigned to "natural" schools of investigation
SATIRE of Royal Society: experimental and natural philosophy (macro/micro)
Lots of Q&A and Empress' decree that science must be **UTILITARIAN**
Science and Philosophy exist to ARGUE / DIVIDE
Therefore, keep Scientists and Philosophers away from Religion and Politics!

Section III: Spiritual Discourse
Women put in charge of religion
The Two Chapels: TERROR (Fire-Stones) and COMFORT (Sun-Stones)
Duchess of Newcastle (Cavendish) as Empress's scribe (female for female)
"Autobiography" of the Cavendish family following the English Civil War
METALITERARY self-creation / world-creation / shared spirit-intelligence

PART II: Naval battle on Earth to "save" her homeland (EFSI, a part of the **BLINKING WORLD**)
Use of Blazing World resources / science (fire-stones, submarines,
Proto-SF battle
UTILITY OF SCIENCE!
End with games and contests: peace

EPILOGUE: On the power of **AUTHORIAL CREATION**

THE DESCRIPTION OF A NEW WORLD, CALLED THE BLAZING WORLD (1666)

MARGARET CAVENDISH, DUCHESS OF NEWCASTLE (1623-1673)

Margaret "Mad Madge" Cavendish (the Duchess of Newcastle) was a Renaissance aristocrat / Royalist / eccentric / writer who wrote liberally (and publically) on matters scientific and philosophical in all major genres: POETRY, PROSE, and DRAMA were employed to express her many innovative—and often controversial—ideas about Natural Philosophy. She was the first—and last—Renaissance woman to be invited to attend a meeting of the Royal Society of London.

Cavendish is—importantly—often credited with writing the first sustained work of science fiction: The Description of a New World, Called the Blazing World *(1666). This UTOPIAN "parallel world" story—whether defined as "science fiction" or "proto-science fiction"—is densely packed with novel ideas on philosophy, metaphysics, natural science, religion, and gender roles; it is less than packed with plot: the heroine travels to new world, argues politely with its weird animal-hybrid inhabitants, and briefly returns to her native Blinking World to kick ass with advanced weaponry (jet engines and submarines!). Along the way, Cavendish SATIRIZES the Royal Society, promotes UTILITARIANISM, argues for a reorganization of religion, endorses female leadership and Platonic friendship, theorizes about astral projection, and METALITERARILY inserts herself (and her family's financial concerns) into her own creative text.* Blazing World *is a tour de force of ideas, if not structure (although it is well to remember that formal structure was seldom Cavendish's primary concern: she treated all literary forms as conduits for her prodigious creative and critical thought).*

Cavendish is sometimes regarded as an early feminist (by virtue of her outspoken criticism of established "Men of Science" and her unapologetically non-conformist attitude/attire/language), although—like her pioneering work of "science fiction"—it may be more accurate to consider her a "proto-feminist."

A Merchant travelling into a foreign Country, fell extreamly in Love with a young Lady; but being a stranger in that Nation, and beneath her, both in Birth and Wealth, he could have but little hopes of obtaining his desire; however his Love growing more and more vehement upon him, even to the slighting of all difficulties, he resolved at last to Steal her away; which he had the better opportunity to do, because her Father's house was not far from the Sea, and she often using to gather shells upon the shore accompanied not with above two to three of her servants it encouraged him the more to execute his design. Thus coming one time with a little leight Vessel, not unlike a Packet-boat, mann'd with some few Sea-men, and well victualled, for fear of some accidents, which might perhaps retard their journey, to the place where she used to repair; he forced her away: But when he fancied himself the happiest man of the World, he proved to be the most unfortunate; for Heaven frowning at his Theft, raised such a Tempest, as they knew not what to do, or whither to steer their course; so that the Vessel, both by its own leightness, and the violent motion of the Wind, was carried as swift as an Arrow out of a Bow, towards the North-pole, and in a short time reached the Icy Sea, where the wind forced it amongst huge pieces of Ice; but being little, and leight, it did by the assistance and favour of the gods to this virtuous Lady, so turn and wind through those precipices, as if it had been guided by some experienced Pilot, and skilful Mariner: But alas! Those few men which were in it, not knowing whither they went, nor what was to be done in so strange an Adventure, and not being provided for so cold a Voyage, were all frozen to death; the young Lady onely, by the light of her Beauty, the heat of her Youth, and Protection of the Gods, remaining alive: Neither was it a wonder that the men did freeze to death; for they were not onely driven to the very end or point of the Pole of that World, but even to another Pole of another World, which joined close to it; so that the cold having a double strength at the conjunction of those two Poles, was insupportable: At last, the Boat still passing on, was forced into another World; for it is impossible to round this Worlds Globe from Pole to Pole, so as we do from East to West; because the Poles of the other World, joining to the Poles of this, do not allow any further passage to surround the World that way; but if any one arrives to either of these Poles, he is either forced to return, or to enter into another World: and lest you should scruple at it, and think, if it were thus, those that live at the Poles would either see two Suns at one time, or else they would never want the Sun's light for six months together, as it is commonly believed: You must know, that each of these Worlds having its own Sun to enlighten it, they move each one in their peculiar Circles; which motion is so just and exact, that neither can hinder or obstruct the other; for they do not exceed their Tropicks: and although they should meet, yet we in this World cannot so well perceive them, by reason of the brightness of our Sun, which being nearer to us, obstructs the splendor of the Sun of the other World, they being too far off to be discerned by our optick perception, except we use very good Telescopes; by which, skilful

Astronomers have often observed two or three Suns at once. But to return to the wandering Boat, and the distresed Lady; she seeing all the Men dead, found small comfort in life; their Bodies which were preserved all that while from putrefaction and stench, by the extremity of cold, began now to thaw, and corrupt; whereupon she having not strength enough to fling them over-board, was forced to remove out of her small Cabine, upon the deck, to avoid the nauseous smell; and finding the Boat swim between two plains of Ice, as a stream that runs betwixt two shores, at last perceived land, but covered all with Snow: from which came, walking upon the Ice, strange Creatures, in shape like Bears, only they went upright as men; those Creatures coming near the Boat, catched hold of it with their Paws, that served them instead of hands; some two or three of them entred first; and when they came out, the rest went in one after another; at last having viewed and observed all that was in the Boat, they spake to each other in a language which the Lady did not understand; and having carried her out of the Boat, sunk it, together with the dead men.

The Lady now finding herself in so strange a place, and amongst such wonderful kind of Creatures, was extreamly strucken with fear, and could entertain no other Thoughts, but that every moment her life was to be a sacrifice to their cruelty; but those Bear-like Creatures, how terrible soever they appear'd to her sight, yet were they so far from exercising any cruelty upon her, that rather they shewed her all civility and kindness imaginable; for she being not able to go upon the Ice, by reason of its slipperiness, they took her up in their rough arms, and carried her into their City, where instead of Houses, they had Caves underground; and as soon as they enter'd the City, both Males and Females, young and old, flockt together to see this Lady, holding up their Paws in admiration; at last having brought her into a certain large and spacious Cave, which they intended for her reception, they left her to the custody of the Females, who entertained her with all kindness and respect, and gave her such victuals as they used to eat; but seeing her Constitution neither agreed with the temper of that Climate, nor their Diet, they were resolved to carry her into another Island of a warmer temper; in which were men like Foxes, onely walking in an upright shape, who received their neighbours the Bear-men with great civility and Courtship, very much admiring this beauteous Lady; and having discoursed some while together, agreed at last to make her a Present to the Emperor of their World; to which end, after she had made some short stay in the same place, they brought her cross that Island to a large River, whose stream run smooth and clear, like Chrystal; in which were numerous Boats, much like our Fox-traps; in one whereof she was carried, some of the Bear- and Fox-men waiting on her; and as soon as they had crossed the River, they came into an Island where there were Men which had heads, beaks and feathers, like wild-Geese, onely they went in an upright shape, like the Bear-men and Fox-men: their rumps they carried between their legs, their wings were of the same length with their Bodies, and their tails of an indifferent size, trailing after them like a Ladie's Garment; and after the Bear- and Fox-men had declared their intention and design to their Neighbours, the Geese- or Bird-men, some of them joined to the rest, and attended the Lady through that Island, till they came to another great and large River, where there was a preparation made of many Boats, much like Birds nests, onely of a bigger size; and having crost that River, they arrived into another Island, which was of a pleasant and mild temper, full of Woods and the Inhabitants thereof were Satyrs, who received both the Bear- Fox- and Bird men, with all respect and civility; and after some conferences (for they all understood each others language) some chief of the Satyrs joining to them, accompanied the Lady out of that Island to another River, wherein were many handsome and commodious Barges; and having crost that River, they entered into a large and spacious Kingdom, the men whereof were of a Grass-Green Complexion, who entertained them very kindly, and provided all conveniences for their further voyage: hitherto they had onely crost Rivers, but now they could not avoid the open Seas any longer; wherefore they made their Ships and tacklings ready to sail over into the Island, where the Emperor of the Blazing- world (for so it was call'd) kept his residence. Very good Navigators they were; and though they had no knowledg of the Load-stone, or Needle or pendulous Watches, yet (which was as serviceable to them) they had subtile observations, and great practice; in so much that they could not onely tell the depth of the Sea in every place, but where there were shelves of Sand, Rocks, and other obstructions to be avoided by skilful and experienced Sea-men: Besides, they were excellent Augurers, which skill they counted more necessary and beneficial then the use of Compasses, Cards, Watches, and the like; but, above the rest, they had an extraordinary Art, much to be taken notice of by Experimental Philosophers, and that was a certain Engin, which would draw in a great quantity of Air, and shoot forth Wind with a great force; this Engine in a calm, they placed behind their Ships, and in a storm, before; for it served against the raging waves, like Cannons against an hostile Army, or besieged Town; it would batter and beat the waves in pieces, were they as high as Steeples; and as soon as a breach was made, they forced their passage through, in spight even of the most furious wind, using two of those Engins at every Ship, one before, to beat off the waves, and another behind to drive it on; so that the artificial wind had the better of the natural; for, it had a greater advantage of the waves, then the natural of the Ships: the natural being above the face of the Water, could not without a down right motion enter or press into the Ships; whereas the artificial with a sideward-motion, did pierce into the bowels of the Waves: Moreover, it is to be observed, that in a great Tempest they would join their Ships in battel-aray: and when they feared Wind and Waves would be too strong for them, if they divided their Ships; they joined as many together as the compass or advantage of the places of the Liquid Element would give them leave. For, their Ships were so ingeniously contrived, that they could fasten them together as close as a Honey-comb, without waste of place; and being thus united, no Wind nor Waves were able to separate them. The Emperor's Ships, were all of Gold; but the Merchants and Skippers, of Leather; the Golden Ships were not much heavier then ours of Wood, by reason they were neatly made, and required not such thickness, neither were they troubled with Pitch, Tar, Pumps, Guns, and the like, which make our Woodden-Ships very heavy; for though they were not all of a piece, yet they were so well sodder'd, that there was no fear of Leaks, Chinks, or Clefts; and as for Guns, there was no use of them, because they had no other enemies but the Winds: But the Leather Ships were not altogether so sure, although much leighter; besides, they were pitched to keep out Water.

Having thus prepar'd, and order'd their Navy, they went on in despight of Calm or Storm: And though the Lady at first fancied her self in a very sad condition, and her mind was much tormented with doubts and fears, not knowing whether this strange Adventure would tend to her safety or destruction; yet she being withal of a generous spirit, and ready wit, considering what dangers she had past, and finding those sorts of men civil and diligent attendants to her, took courage, and endeavoured to learn their language; which after she had obtained so far, that partly by some words and signs she was able to apprehend their meaning, she was so far from being afraid of them, that she thought her self not onely safe, but very happy in their company: By which we may see, that Novelty discomposes the mind, but acquaintance settles it in peace and tranquillity. At last, having passed by several rich Islands and Kingdoms, they went towards Paradise, which was the seat of the Emperor; and coming in sight of it, rejoiced very much; the Lady at first could perceive nothing but high Rocks, which seemed to touch the Skies; and although they appear'd not of an equal heigth, yet they seemed to be all one piece, without partitions: but at last drawing nearer, she perceived a clift, which was a part of those Rocks, out of which she spied coming forth a great number of Boats, which afar off shewed like a company of Ants, marching one after another; the Boats appeared like the holes or partitions in a Honey-comb, and when joined together, stood as close; the men were of several Complexions, but none like any of our World; and when both the Boats and Ships met, they saluted and spake to each other very courteously; for there was but one language in all that World: nor no more but one Emperor, to whom they all submitted with the greatest duty and obedience, which made them live in a continued Peace and Happiness; not acquainted with Foreign Wars or Home-bred Insurrections. The Lady now being arrived at this place, was carried out of her Ship into one of those Boats, and conveighed through the same passage (for there was no other) into that part of the World where the Emperor did reside; which part was very pleasant, and of a mild temper: Within it self it was divided by a great number of vast and large Rivers, all ebbing and flowing, into several Islands of unequal distance from each other, which in most parts were as pleasant, healthful, rich, and fruitful, as Nature could make them; and, as I mentioned before, secure from all Foreign Invasions, by reason there was but one way to enter, and that like a Labyrinth, so winding and turning among the Rocks, that no other Vessels but small Boats, could pass, carrying not above three passengers at a time: On each side all along the narrow and winding River, there were several Cities, some of Marble, some of Alabaster, some of Agat, some of Amber, some of Coral, and some of other precious materials not known in our world; all which after the Lady had passed, she came to the Imperial City, named Paradise, which appeared in form like several Islands; for, Rivers did run betwixt every street, which together with the Bridges, whereof there was a great number, were all paved. The City it self was built of Gold; and their Architectures were noble, stately, and magnificent, not like our Modern, but like those in the Romans time; for, our Modern Buildings are like those Houses which Children use to make of Cards, one story above another, fitter for Birds, then Men; but theirs were more Large, and Broad, then high; the highest of them did not exceed two stories, besides those rooms that were under-ground, as Cellars, and other Offices. The Emperor's Palace stood upon an indifferent ascent from the Imperial City; at the top of which ascent was a broad Arch, supported by several Pillars, which went round the Palace, and contained four of our English miles in compass: within the Arch stood the Emperor's Guard, which consisted of several sorts of Men; at every half mile, was a Gate to enter, and every Gate was of a different fashion; the first, which allowed a passage from the Imperial City into the Palace, had on either hand a Cloyster, the outward part whereof stood upon Arches sustained by Pillars, but the inner part was close: Being entred through the Gate, the Palace it self appear'd in its middle like the Isle of a Church, a mile and a half long, and half a mile broad; the roof of it was all Arched, and rested upon Pillars, so artificially placed that a stranger would lose himself therein without a Guide; at the extream sides, that is, between the outward and inward part

of the Cloyster, were Lodgings for Attendants; and in the midst of the
Palace, the Emperor's own Rooms; whose Lights were placed at the top
of every one, because of the heat of the Sun: the Emperor's appartment
for State was no more inclosed then the rest; onely an Imperial Throne
was in every appartment, of which the several adornments could not be
perceived until one entered, because the Pillars were so just opposite to
one another, that all the adornments could not be seen at one. The first part
of the Palace was, as the Imperial City, all of Gold; and when it came to the
Emperors appartment, it was so rich with Diamonds, Pearls, Rubies, and
the like precious Stones, that it surpasses my skill to enumerate them all.
Amongst the rest, the Imperial Room of State appear'd most magnificent;
it was paved with green Diamonds (for there are in that World Diamonds
of all Colours) so artificially, as it seemed but of one piece; the Pillars
were set with Diamonds so close, and in such a manner, that they appear'd
most Glorious to the sight; between every Pillar was a Bow or Arch of
a certain sort of Diamonds, the like whereof our World does not afford;
which being placed in every one of the Arches in several rows, seemed
just like so many Rain-bows of several different colours. The roof of the
Arches was of blew Diamonds, and in the midst thereof was a Carbuncle,
which represented the Sun; and the Rising and Setting-Sun at the East and
West-side of the Room were made of Rubies. Out of this Room there was
a passage into the Emperor's Bed-Chamber, the Walls whereof were of
Jet, and the Floor of black Marble; the Roof was of Mother of Pearl, where
the Moon and Blazing-Stars were represented by white Diamonds, and his
Bed was made of Diamonds and Carbuncles.

No sooner was the Lady brought before the Emperor, but he conceived
her to be some Goddess, and offered to worship her; which she refused,
telling him, (for by that time she had pretty well learned their Language)
that although she came out of another world, yet was she but a mortal. At
which the Emperor rejoycing, made her his Wife, and gave her an absolute
power to rule and govern all that World as she pleased. But her subjects,
who could hardly be perswaded to believe her mortal, tender'd her all the
Veneration and Worship due to a Deity.

Her Accoustrement after she was made Empress, was as followeth: On her
head she wore a Cap of Pearl, and a Half-moon of Diamonds just before
it; on the top of her Crown came spreading over a broad Carbuncle, cut
in the form of the Sun; her Coat was of Pearl, mixt with blew Diamonds,
and frindged with red ones; her Buskins and Sandals were of green
Diamonds; In her left hand she held a Buckler, to signifie the Defence of
her Dominions; which Buckler was made of that sort of Diamond as has
several different Colours; and being cut and made in the form of an Arch,

shewed like a Rain-bow; In her right hand she carried a Spear made of white Diamond, cut like the tail of a Blazing Star, which signified that she was ready to assault those that proved her Enemies.

None was allowed to use or wear Gold but those of the Imperial Race, which were the onely Nobles of the State; nor durst any one wear Jewels but the Emperor, the Empress and their Eldest Son; notwithstanding that they had an infinite quantity both of Gold and precious Stones in that World; for they had larger extents of Gold, then our Arabian Sands; their precious Stones were Rocks, and their Diamonds of several Colours; they used no Coyn, but all their Traffick was by exchange of several Commodities.

Their Priests and Governors were Princes of the Imperial Blood, and made Eunuches for that purpose; and as for the ordinary sort of men in that part of the World where the Emperor resided, they were of several Complexions; not white, black, tawny, olive or ash-coloured; but some appear'd of an Azure, some of a deep Purple, some of a Grass-green, some of a Scarlet, some of an Orange-colour, &c. Which Colours and Complexions, whether they were made by the bare reflection of light, without the assistance of small particles; or by the help of well-ranged and order'd Atoms; or by a continual agitation of little Globules; or by some pressing and re-acting motion, I am not able to determine. The rest of the Inhabitants of that World, were men of several different sorts, shapes, figures, dispositions, and humors, as I have already made mention, heretofore; some were Bear-men, some Worm-men, some Fish- or Mear-men, otherwise called Syrens; some Bird-men, some Fly-men, some Ant-men, some Geese-men, some Spider-men, some Lice-men, some Fox-men, some Ape-men, some Jack daw-men, some Magpie-men, some Parrot-men, some Satyrs, some Gyants, and many more, which I cannot all remember; and of these several sorts of men, each followed such a profession as was most proper for the nature of their Species, which the Empress encouraged them in, especially those that had applied themselves to the study of several Arts and Sciences; for they were as ingenious and witty in the invention of profitable and useful Arts, as we are in our world, nay, more; and to that end she erected Schools, and founded several Societies. The Bear-men were to be her Experimental Philosophers, the Bird-men her Astronomers, the Fly- Worm- and Fish-men her Natural Philosophers, the Ape-men her Chymists, the Satyrs her Galenick Physicians, the Fox-men her Politicians, the Spider- and Lice-men her Mathematicians, the Jackdaw- Magpie- and Parrot-men her Orators and Logicians, the Gyants her Architects, &c. But before all things, she having got a Soveraign power from the Emperor over all the World, desired to be informed both of the manner of their Religion and Government; and to that end she called the Priests and States men, to give her an account of either. Of the States men she enquired, first, Why they had so few Laws? To which they answered, That many Laws made many Divisions, which most commonly did breed Factions, and at last brake out into open Wars. Next, she asked, Why they preferred the Monarchical form of Government before any other? They answered, That as it was natural for one Body to have but one Head, so it was also natural for a Politick body to have but one Governor; and that a Common-wealth, which had many Governors was like a Monster with many Heads. Besides, said they, a Monarchy is a divine form of Government, and agrees most with our Religion: For as there is but one God, whom we all unanimously worship and adore with one Faith; so we are resolved to have but one Emperor, to whom we all submit with one obedience.

Then the Empress seeing that the several sorts of her Subjects had each their Churches apart, asked the Priests, whether they were of several Religions? They answered her Majesty, That there was no more but one Religion in all that World, nor no diversity of opinions in that same Religion for though there were several sorts of men, yet had they all but one opinion concerning the Worship and Adoration of God. The Empress asked them, Whether they were Jews, Turks, or Christians? We do not know, said they, what Religions those are; but we do all unanimously acknowledg, worship and adore the Onely, Omnipotent, and Eternal God, with all reverence, submission, and duty. Again, the Empress enquired, Whether they had several Forms of Worship? They answered, No: For our Devotion and Worship consists onely in Prayers, which we frame according to our several Necessities, in Petitions, Humiliations, Thanksgiving, &c. Truly, replied the Empress, I thought you had been either Jews, or Turks, because I never perceived any Women in your Congregations: But what is the reason, you bar them from your religious Assemblies? It is not fit, said they, that Men and Women should be promiscuously together in time of Religious Worship; for their company hinders Devotion, and makes many, instead of praying to God, direct their Devotion to their Mistresses. But, asked the Empress, Have they no Congregation of their own, to perform the duties of Divine Worship, as well as Men? No, answered they: but they stay at home, and say their Prayers by themselves in their Closets. Then the Empress desir'd to know the reason why the Priests and Governors of their World were made Eunuchs? They answer'd, To keep them from Marriage: For Women and Children most commonly make disturbance both in Church and State. But, said she, Women and Children have no Employment in Church or State. 'Tis true, answer'd they; but, although they are not admitted to publick Employments, yet are they so prevalent with their Husbands and Parents, that many times by their importunate perswasions, they cause as much, nay, more mischief secretly, then if they had the management of publick Affairs.

The Empress having received an information of what concerned both Church and State, passed some time in viewing the Imperial Palace, where she admired much the skil and ingenuity of the Architects, and enquired of them, first, Why they built their Houses no higher then two stories from the Ground? They answered her Majesty, That the lower their Buildings were, the less were they subject either to the heat of the Sun, or Wind, Tempest, Decay, &c. Then she desired to know the reason, why they made them so thick? They answered, That, the thicker the Walls were, the warmer they were in Winter, the cooler in Summer; for their thickness kept out both the Cold and Heat. Lastly, she asked, Why they Arched their Roofs, and made so many Pillars? They replied, That Arches and Pillars, did not onely grace a Building very much, and caused it to appear Magnificent, but made it also firm and lasting.

The Empress was very well satisfied with their answers; and after some time, when she thought that her new founded societies of the Vertuoso's had made a good progress in the several Employments she had put them upon, she caused a Convocation first of the Bird-men, and commanded them to give her a true relation of the two Cœlestial Bodies, viz. the Sun and Moon, which they did with all the obedience and faithfulness befitting their duty.

The Sun, as much as they could observe, they related to be a firm or solid Stone, of a vast bigness; of colour yellowish, and of an extraordinary splendor: But the Moon, they said, was of a whitish colour; and although she looked dim in the presence of the Sun, yet had she her own light, and was a shining body of her self, as might be perceived by her vigorous appearance in Moon-shiny-nights; the difference onely betwixt her own and the Sun's light was, that the Sun did strike his beams in a direct line; but the Moon never respected the Centre of their World in a right line, but her Centre was always excentrical. The Spots both in the Sun and Moon, as far as they were able to perceive, they affirmed to be nothing else but flaws and stains of their stony Bodies. Concerning the heat of the Sun, they were not of one opinion; some would have the Sun hot in it self, alledging an old Tradition, that it should at some time break asunder, and burn the Heavens, and consume this world into hot Embers, which, said they, could not be done, if the Sun were not fiery of it self. Others again said, This opinion could not stand with reason; for Fire being a destroyer of all things, the Sun-stone after this manner would burn up all the near adjoining Bodies: Besides, said they, Fire cannot subsist without fuel; and the Sunstone having nothing to feed on, would in a short time consume it self; wherefore they thought it more probable that the Sun was not actually hot, but onely by the reflection of its light; so that its heat was an effect of its light, both being immaterial. But this opinion again was laught at by others, and rejected as ridiculous, who thought it impossible that one immaterial should produce another; and believed that both the light and heat of the Sun proceeded from a swift Circular motion of the Æthereal Globules, which by their striking upon the Optick nerve, caused light, and their motion produced heat: But neither would this opinion hold; for, said some, then it would follow, that the sight of Animals is the cause of light; and that, were there no eyes, there would be no light; which was against all sense and reason. Thus they argued concerning the heat and light of the Sun; but, which is remarkable, none did say, that the Sun was a Globous fluid body, and had a swift Circular motion; but all agreed, It was fixt and firm like a Center, and therefore they generally called it the Sun-stone.

Then the Empress asked them the reason, Why the Sun and Moon did often appear in different postures or shapes, as sometimes magnified, sometimes diminished; sometimes elevated, otherwhiles depressed; now thrown to the right, and then to the left? To which some of the Bird-men answered, That it proceeded from the various degrees of heat and cold, which are found in the Air, from whence did follow a differing density and rarity; and likewise from the vapours that are interposed, whereof those that ascend are higher and less dense then the ambient air, but those which descend are heavier and more dense. But others did with more probability affirm, that it was nothing else but the various patterns of the Air; for like as Painters do not copy out one and the same original just alike at all times; so, said they, do several parts of the Air make different patterns of the luminous Bodies of the Sun and Moon: which patterns, as several copies, the sensitive motions do figure out in the substance of our eyes.

This answer the Empress liked much better then the former, and enquired further, What opinion they had of those Creatures that are called the motes of the Sun? To which they answered, That they were nothing else but streams of very small, rare and transparent particles, through which the Sun was represented as through a glass: for if they were not transparent, said they, they would eclipse the light of the Sun; and if not rare and of an airy substance, they would hinder Flies from flying in the Air, at least retard their flying motion: Nevertheless, although they were thinner then the thinnest vapour, yet were they not so thin as the body of air, or else they would not be perceptible by animal sight. Then the Empress asked, Whether they were living Creatures? They answered, Yes: Because they did encrease and decrease, and were nourished by the presence, and starved by the absence of the Sun.

Having thus finished their discourse of the Sun and Moon, the Empress desired to know what Stars there were besides? But they answer'd, that they could perceive in that World none other but Blazing Stars, and from thence it had the name that it was called the Blazing-World; and these Blazing-Stars, said they, were such solid, firm and shining bodies as the Sun and Moon, not of a Globular, but of several sorts of figures: some had tails; and some, other kinds of shapes.

After this, The Empress asked them, What kind of substance or creature the Air was? The Bird-men answered, That they could have no other perception of the Air, but by their own Respiration: For, said they, some bodies are onely subject to touch, others onely to sight, and others onely to smell; but some are subject to none of our exterior Senses: For Nature is so full of variety, that our weak Senses cannot perceive all the various sorts of her Creatures; neither is there any one object perceptible by all our Senses, no more then several objects are by one sense. I believe you, replied the Empress; but if you can give no account of the Air, said she, you will hardly be able to inform me how Wind is made; for they say, that Wind is nothing but motion of the Air. The Bird-men answer'd, That they observed Wind to be more dense then Air, and therefore subject to the sense of Touch; but what properly Wind was, and the manner how it was made, they could not exactly tell; some said, it was caused by the Clouds falling on each other; and others, that it was produced of a hot and dry exhalation: which ascending, was driven down again by the coldness of the Air that is in the middle Region, and by reason of its leightness, could not go directly to the bottom, but was carried by the Air up and down: Some would have it a flowing Water of the Air; and others again, a flowing Air moved by the blaz of the Stars.

But the Empress, seeing they could not agree concerning the cause of Wind, asked, Whether they could tell how Snow was made? To which they answered That according to their observation, Snow was made by a commixture of Water, and some certain extract of the Element of Fire that is under the Moon; a small portion of which extract, being mixed with Water, and beaten by Air or Wind, made a white Froth called Snow; which being after some while dissolved by the heat of the same spirit, turned to Water again. This observation amazed the Empress very much; for she had hitherto believed, That Snow was made by cold motions, and not by such an agitation or beating of a fiery extract upon water: Nor could she be perswaded to believe it until the Fish- or Mear-men had delivered their observation upon the making of Ice, which, they said, was not produced, as some hitherto conceived, by the motion of the Air, raking the Superficies of the Earth, but by some strong saline vapour arising out of the Seas, which condensed Water into Ice; and the more quantity there was of that vapour, the greater were the Mountains of Precipices of Ice; but the reason that it did not so much freeze in the Torrid Zone, or under the Ecliptick, as near or under the Poles, was, that this vapour in those places being drawn up by the Sun-beams into the middle Region of the Air, was onely condensed into Water, and fell down in showres of Rain; when as, under the Poles, the heat of the Sun being not so vehement, the same vapour had no force or power to rise so high, and therefore caused so much Ice, by ascending and acting onely upon the surface of water.

This Relation confirmed partly the observation of the Bird-men concerning the cause of Snow; but since they had made mention that that same extract, which by its commixture with Water made Snow, proceeded from the Element of Fire, that is under the Moon: The Emperess asked them, of what nature that Elementary Fire was; whether it was like ordinary Fire here upon Earth, or such a Fire as is within the bowels of the Earth, and as the famous Mountains Vesuvius and Ætna do burn withal; or whether it was such a sort of fire, as is found in flints, &c. They answered, That the Elementary Fire, which is underneath the Sun, was not so solid as any of those mentioned fires; because it had no solid fuel to feed on; but yet it was much like the flame of ordinary fire, onely somewhat more thin and fluid; for Flame, said they, is nothing else but the airy part of a fired Body.

Lastly, the Empress asked the Bird-men of the nature of Thunder and Lightning? and whether it was not caused by roves of Ice falling upon each other? To which they answered, That it was not made that way, but by an encounter of cold and heat; so that an exhalation being kindled in the Clouds, did dash forth Lightning, and that there were so many rentings of Clouds as there were Sounds and Cracking noises: But this opinion was contradicted by others, who affirmed that Thunder was a sudden and monstrous Blaz, stirred up in the Air, and did not always require a Cloud; but the Empress not knowing what they meant by Blaz (for even they themselves were not able to explain the sense of this word) liked the former better; and, to avoid hereafter tedious disputes, and have the truth of the Phænomena's of Cœlestial Bodies more exactly known, commanded the Bear-men, which were her Experimental Philosophers, to observe them through such Instruments as are called Telescopes, which they did according to her Majesties Command; but these Telescopes caused more differences and divisions amongst them, then ever they had before; for some said, they perceived that the Sun stood still, and the Earth did move about it; others were of opinion, that they both did move; and others said again, that the Earth stood still, and Sun did move; some counted more Stars then others; some discovered new Stars never seen before; some fell into a great dispute with others concerning the bigness of the Stars; some said, The Moon was another World like their Terrestrial Globe, and the spots therein were Hills and Vallies; but others would have the spots to be the Terrestrial parts, and the smooth and glossie parts, the Sea: At last, the Empress commanded them to go with their Telescopes to the very end of the Pole that was joined to the World she came from, and try whether they could perceive any Stars in it: which they did; and, being returned to her Majesty, reported that they had seen three Blazing-Stars appear there, one after another in a short time, whereof two were bright, and one dim; but they could not agree neither in this observation: for some said, It was but one Star which appeared at three several times, in several places; and others would have them to be three several Stars; for they thought it impossible, that those three several appearances should have been but one Star, because every Star did rise at a certain time, and appear'd in a certain place, and did disappear in the same place: Next, It is altogether improbable, said they, That one Star should fly from place to place, especially at such a vast distance, without a visible motion; in so short a time, and appear in such different places, whereof two were quite opposite, and the third side-ways: Lastly, If it had been but one Star, said they, it would always have kept the same splendor, which it did not; for, as above mentioned, two were bright, and one was dim. After they had thus argued, the Empress began to grow angry at their Telescopes, that they could give no better Intelligence; for, said she, now I do plainly perceive, that your Glasses are false Informers, and instead of discovering the Truth, delude your Senses; Wherefore I Command you to break them, and let the Bird-men trust onely to their natural eyes, and examine Cœlestial Objects by the motions of their own Sense and Reason. The Bear-men replied, That it was not the fault of their Glasses, which caused such differences in their Opinions, but the sensitive motions in their Optick organs did not move alike, nor were their rational judgments always regular: To which the Empress answered, That if their Glasses were true Informers, they would rectifie their irregular Sense and Reason; But, said she, Nature has made your Sense and Reason more regular then Art has your Glasses; for they are meer deluders, and will never lead you to the knowledg of Truth; Wherefore I command you again to break them; for you may observe the progressive motions of Cœlestial Bodies with your natural eyes better then through Artificial Glasses. The Bear-men being exceedingly troubled at her Majesties displeasure concerning their Telescopes, kneel'd down, and in the humblest manner petitioned, that they might not be broken; for, said they, we take more delight in Artificial delusions, then in Natural truths. Besides, we shall want Imployments for our Senses, and Subjects for Arguments; for, were there nothing but truth, and no falshood, there would be no occasion to dispute, and by this means we should want the aim and pleasure of our endeavors in confuting and contradicting each other; neither would one man be thought wiser then another, but all would either be alike knowing and wise, or all would be fools; wherefore we most humbly beseech your Imperial Majesty to spare our Glasses, which are our onely delight, and as dear to us as our lives. The Empress at last consented to their request, but upon condition, that their disputes and quarrels should remain within their Schools, and cause no factions or disturbances in State, or Government. The Bear-men, full of joy, returned their most humble thanks to the Empress; and to make her amends for the displeasure which their Telescopes had occasioned, told her Majesty, that they had several other artificial Optick-Glasses, which they were sure would give her Majesty a great deal more satisfaction. Amongst the rest, they brought forth several Microscopes, by the means of which they could enlarge the shapes of little bodies, and make a Lowse appear as big as an Elephant, and a Mite as big as a Whale. First of all they shewed the Empress a gray Drone-flye, wherein they observed that the greatest part of her face, nay, of her head, consisted of two large bunches all cover'd over with a multitude of small Pearls or Hemispheres in a Trigonal order: Which Pearls were of two degrees, smaller and bigger; the smaller degree was lowermost, and looked towards the ground; the other was upward, and looked sideward, forward and backward: They were all so smooth and polished, that they were able to represent the image of any object, the number of them was in all 14000. After the view of this strange and miraculous Creature, and their several observations upon it, the Empress asked them, What they judged those little Hemispheres might be? They answered, That each of them was a perfect Eye, by reason they perceived that each was covered with a Transparent Cornea, containing a liquor within them, which resembled the watery or glassie humor of the Eye. To which the Emperess replied, That they might be glassie Pearls, and yet not Eyes; and that perhaps their Microscopes did not truly inform them. But they smilingly answered her Majesty, That she did not know the vertue of those Microscopes: for they never delude, but rectifie and inform the Senses; nay, the World, said they, would be but blind without them, as it has been in former ages before those Microscopes were invented.

After this, they took a Charcoal, and viewing it with one of their best Microscopes, discovered in it an infinite multitude of pores, some bigger, some less; so close and thick, that they left but very little space betwixt them to be filled with a solid body; and to give her Imperial Majesty a better assurance thereof, they counted in a line of them an inch long, no less then 2700 pores; from which Observation they drew this following Conclusion, to wit, That this multitude of pores was the cause of the blackness of the Coal; for, said they, a body that has so many pores, from each of which no light is reflected, must necessarily look black, since black is nothing else but a privation of light, or a want of reflection. But the Empress replied, That if all Colours were made by reflection of light, and that Black was as much a colour as any other colour; then certainly they contradicted themselves in saying that black was made by want of reflection. However, not to interrupt your Microscopical Inspections, said she, let us see how Vegetables appear through your Glasses; whereupon they took a Nettle, and by the vertue of the Microscope, discovered that underneath the points of the Nettle there were certain little bags or bladders, containing a poysonous liquor, and when the points had made way into the interior parts of the skin, they like Syringe-pipes served to conveigh that same liquor into them. To which Observation the Empress replied, That if there were such poyson in Nettles, then certainly in eating of them, they would hurt us inwardly, as much as they do outwardly? But they answered, That it belonged to Physicians more then to Experimental Philosophers, to give Reasons hereof; for they only made Microscopical inspections, and related the Figures of the Natural parts of Creatures acording to the representation of their glasses.

Lastly, They shewed the Empress a Flea, and a Lowse; which Creatures through the Microscope appear'd so terrible to her sight, that they had almost put her into a swoon; the description of all their parts would be very tedious to relate, and therefore I'le forbear it at this present. The Empress, after the view of those strangely-shaped Creatures, pitied much those that are molested with them, especially poor Beggars, which although they have nothing to live on themselves, are yet necessitated to maintain and feed of their own flesh and blood, a company of such terrible Creatures called Lice; who, instead of thanks, do reward them with pains, and torment them for giving them nourishment and food. But after the Empress had seen the shapes of these monstrous Creatures, she desir'd to know, Whether their Microscopes could hinder their biting, or at least shew some means how to avoid them? To which they answered, That such Arts were mechanical and below the noble study of Microscopical observations. Then the Empress asked them, Whether they had not such sorts of Glasses that could enlarge and magnifie the shapes of great Bodies as well as they had done of little ones? Whereupon they took one of their best and largest Microscopes, and endeavoured to view a Whale thorow it; but alas! the shape of the Whale was so big, that its Circumference went beyond the magnifying quality of the Glass; whether the error proceeded from the Glass, or from a wrong position of the Whale against the reflection of light, I cannot certainly tell. The Empress seeing the insufficiency of those Magnifying-Glasses, that they were not able to enlarge all sorts of Objects, asked the Bear-men, whether they could not make Glasses of a contrary nature to those they had shewed her, to wit, such as instead of enlarging or magnifying the shape or figure of an Object, could contract it beneath its natural proportion: Which, in obedience to her Majesties Commands, they did; and viewing through one of the best of them, a huge and mighty Whale appear'd no bigger then a Sprat; nay, through some no bigger then a Vinegar-Eele; and through their ordinary ones, an Elephant seemed no bigger then a Flea; a Camel no bigger then a Lowse; and an Ostrich no bigger then a Mite. To relate all their Optick observations through the several sorts of their Glasses, would be a tedious work, and tire even the most patient Reader, wherefore I'le pass them by; onely this was very remarkable and worthy to be taken notice of, that notwithstanding their great skil, industry and ingenuity in Experimental Philosophy, they could yet by no means contrive such Glasses, by the help of which they could spy out a Vacuum, with all its dimensions, nor Immaterial substances, Non-beings, and Mixt-beings, or such as are between something and nothing; which they were very much troubled at, hoping that yet, in time, by long study and practice, they might perhaps attain to it.

[*After this, the Empress questions Bird-men, Bear-men, Syrens (Fish-men), and Worm-men regarding their understanding of the air, earth, and sea, as well as creation and climate. Then she grills her Ape-men on chemistry and transmutations, followed by a discussion of herbalism, anatomy (including Monsters!), and disease. As with most of her investigations, the Empress is sometimes dubious of the value of any enquiry unless it produces practical (UTILITARIAN) usage.*]

The Empress having hitherto spent her time in the Examination of the Bird- Fish- Worm- and Ape- men, &c. and received several Intelligences from their several imployments; at last had a mind to divert herself after her serious Discourses, and therefore she sent for the Spider-men, which were her Mathematicians, the Lice-men which were here Geometricians, and the Magpie- Parrot- and Jackdaw-men, which were her Orators and Logicians. The Spider-men came first, and presented her Majesty with a table full of Mathematical points, lines, and figures of all sorts, of squares, circles, triangles, and the like; which the Empress, notwithstanding that she had a very ready wit, and quick apprehension, could not understand; but the more she endeavoured to learn, the more was she confounded: Whether they did ever square the Circle, I cannot exactly tell, nor whether they could make imaginary points and lines; but this I dare say, That their points and lines were so slender, small and thin, that they seem'd next to Imaginary. The Mathematicians were in great esteem with the Empress, as being not onely the chief Tutors and Instructors in many Arts, but some of them excellent Magicians and Informers of spirits, which was the reason their Characters were so abstruse and intricate, that the Emperess knew not what to make of them. There is so much to learn in your Art, said she, that I can neither spare time from other affairs to busie my self in your profession; nor, if I could, do I think I should ever be able to understand your Imaginary points, lines and figures, because they are Non-beings.

Then came the Lice-men, and endeavoured to measure all things to a hairs-breadth, and weigh them to an Atom; but their weights would seldom agree, especially in the weighing of Air, which they found a task impossible to be done; at which the Empress began to be displeased, and told them, that there was neither Truth nor Justice in their Profession; and so dissolved their society.

After this, the Empress was resolved to hear the Magpie- Parrot- and Jackdaw-men, which were her professed Orators and Logicians; whereupon one of the Parrot-men rose with great formality, and endeavoured to make an Eloquent Speech before her Majesty; but before he had half ended, his arguments and divisions being so many, that they caused a great confusion in his brain, he could not go forward, but was forced to retire backward, with great disgrace both to himself, and the whole society; and although one of his brethren endeavoured to second him by another speech, yet was he as far to seek, as the former. At which the Empress appear'd not a little troubled, and told them, That they followed too much the Rules of Art, and confounded themselves with too nice formalities and distinctions; but since I know, said she, that you are a people who have naturally voluble tongues, and good memories; I desire you to consider more the subject you speak of, then your artificial periods, connexions and parts of speech, and leave the rest to your natural Eloquence; which they did, and so became very eminent Orators.

Lastly, her Imperial Majesty being desirous to know what progress her Logicians had made in the Art of disputing, Commanded them to argue upon several Themes or Subjects; which they did; and having made a very nice discourse of Logistical terms and propositions, entred into a dispute by way of Syllogistical Arguments, through all the Figures and Modes: One began with an Argument of the first Mode of the first Figure, thus: Every Politician is wise: Every Knave is a Politician, Therefore every

Knave is wise.

Another contradicted him with a Syllogism of the second Mode of the same Figure, thus: No Politician is wise: Every Knave is a Politician, Therefore no Knave is wise.

The third made an Argument in the third Mode of the same Figure, after this manner: Every Politician is wise: some Knaves are Politicians, Therefore some Knaves are wise.

The Fourth concluded with a Syllogism in the fourth Mode of the same Figure, thus; No Politician is wise: some Knaves are Politicians, Therefore some Knaves are not wise.

After this they took another subject, and one propounded this Syllogism: Every Philosopher is wise: Every Beast is wise, Therefore every Beast is a Philosopher.

But another said that this Argument was false, therefore he contradicted him with a Syllogism of the second Figure of the fourth Mode, thus: Every Philosopher is wise: some Beasts are not wise, Therefore some Beasts are not Philosophers.

Thus they argued, and intended to go on, but the Empress interrupted them: I have enough, said she, of your chopt Logick, and will hear no more of your Syllogisms; for it disorders my Reason, and puts my Brain on the rack; your formal argumentations are able to spoil all natural wit; and I'le have you to consider, that Art does not make Reason, but Reason makes Art; and therefore as much as Reason is above Art, so much is a natural rational discourse to be preferred before an artificial: for Art is, for the most part irregular, and disorders Men's understandings more then it rectifies them, and leads them into a Labyrinth where they'l never get out, and makes them dull and unfit for useful employments; especially your Art of Logick, which consists onely in contradicting each other, in making sophismes, and obscuring Truth, instead of clearing it.

But they replied to her Majesty, That the knowledg of Nature, that is, Natural Philosophy, would be imperfect without the Art of Logick; and that there was an improbable Truth which could no otherwise be found out then by the Art of disputing. Truly, said the Empress, I do believe that it is with Natural Philosophy, as it is with all other effects of Nature; for no particular knowledg can be perfect, by reason knowledg is dividable, as well as composable; nay, to speak properly, Nature her self cannot boast of any perfection, but God himself; because there are so many irregular motions in Nature, and 'tis but a folly to think that Art should be able to regulate them, since Art it self is, for the most part, irregular. But as for Improbable Truth I know not what your meaning is; for Truth is more then Improbability: nay, there is so much difference between Truth and Improbability, that I cannot conceive it possible how they can be joined together. In short, said she, I do no ways approve of your Profession; and though I will not dissolve your society, yet I shall never take delight in hearing you any more; wherefore confine your disputations to your Schools, lest besides the Commonwealth of Learning, they disturb also Divinity and Policy, Religion and Laws, and by that means draw an utter ruine and destruction both upon Church and State.

After the Empress had thus finish'd the Discourses and Conferences with the mentioned societies of her Vertuoso's, she considered by her self the manner of their Religion, and finding it very defective, was troubled, that so wise and knowing a people should have no more knowledg of the Divine Truth; Wherefore she consulted with her own thoughts, whether it was possible to convert them all to her own Religion, and to that end she resolved to build Churches, and make also up a Congregation of Women, whereof she intended to be the head her self, and to instruct them in the several points of her Religion. This she had no sooner begun, but the Women, which generally had quick wits, subtile conceptions, clear understandings, and solid judgments, became, in a short time, very devout and zealous Sisters; for the Empress had an excellent gift of Preaching, and instructing them in the Articles of Faith; and by that means, she converted them not onely soon, but gained an extraordinary love of all her Subjects throughout that World. But at last, pondering with her self the inconstant nature of Mankind, and fearing that in time they would grow weary, and desert the divine Truth, following their own fancies, and living according to their own desires; she began to be troubled that her labours and pains should prove of so little effect, and therefore studied all manner of ways to prevent it. Amongst the rest, she call'd to mind a Relation which the Bird-men made her once, of a Mountain that did burn in flames of fire; and thereupon did immediately send for the wisest and subtilest of her Worm-men, commanding them to discover the cause of the Eruption of that same fire; which they did; and having dived to the very bottom of the Mountain, informed her Majesty, That there was a certain sort of Stone, whose nature was such, that being wetted, it would grow excessively hot, and break forth into a flaming-fire, until it became dry, and then it ceased from burning. The Empress was glad to hear this news, and forthwith desired the Worm men to bring her some of that Stone, but be sure to keep it secret: she sent also for the Bird-men, and asked them whether they could not get her a piece of the Sun- stone? They answered, That it was impossible, unless they did spoil or lessen the light of the World: but, said they, if it please your Majesty, we can demolish one of the numerous Stars of the Sky, which the World will never miss.

The Empress was very well satisfied with this proposal, and having thus imployed these two sorts of men, in the mean while builded two Chappels one above another; the one she lined throughout with Diamonds, both Roof, Walls and Pillars; but the other she resolved to line with the Star-stone; the Fire- stone she placed upon the Diamond-lining, by reason Fire has no power on Diamonds; and when she would have that Chappel where the Fire-stone was, appear all in flame, she had by the means of Artificial pipes, water conveighed into it, which by turning the Cock, did, as out of a Fountain, spring over all the room, and as long as the Fire-stone was wet, the Chappel seemed to be all in a flaming-fire.

The other Chappel, which was lined with the Star- stone, did onely cast a splendorous and comfortable light; both the Chappels stood upon Pillars, just in the middle of a round Cloyster, which was dark as night; neither was there any other light within them, but what came from the Fire- and Star-stone; and being every where open, allowed to all that were within the compass of the Cloyster, a free prospect into them; besides, they were so artificially contrived, that they did both move in a Circle about their own Centres, without intermission, contrary ways. In the Chappel which was lined with the Fire-stone, the Empress preached Sermons of Terror to the wicked, and told them of the punishments for their sins, to wit, That after this life they should be tormented in an everlasting Fire. But in the other Chappel lined with the Star- stone, she preached Sermons of Comfort to those that repented of their sins, and were troubled at their own wickedness: Neither did the heat of the flame in the least hinder her; for the Fire-stone did not cast so great a heat but the Empress was able to endure it, by reason the water which was poured on the Stone, by its own self-motion turned into a flaming-fire, occasioned by the natural motions of the Stone, which made the flame weaker then if it had been fed by some other kind of fuel; the other Chappel where the Star-Stone was, although it did cast a great light, yet was it without all heat, and the Empress appear'd like an Angel in it; and as that Chappel was an embleme of Hell, so this was an embleme of Heaven. And thus the Empress, by Art, and her own Ingenuity, did not onely convert the Blazing-World to her own Religion, but kept them in a constant belief, without inforcement or blood-shed; for she knew well, that belief was a thing not to be forced or pressed upon the people, but to be instilled into their minds by gentle perswasions; and after this manner she encouraged them also in all other duties and employments: for

Fear, though it makes people obey, yet does it not last so long, nor is it so sure a means to keep them to their duties, as Love.

[After this, the Empress attempts to better understand the "framing of her World" by discussing Immaterial Spirits, the Cabbala, Numerology, the Aether, Souls, and Materiality with some Fly-men. Ultimately frustrated by their responses, she "resolved to make a World of her own Invention [...] composed onely of the Rational." In fact, she makes and dissolves "several Worlds" in her mind before consulting the Duchess (Cavendish as character/author) who advises her in the creation of a "proper and useful" world: the perfected Blazing World (although to be honest, the the text is wicked dense at this point). Their immaterial souls then travel together to the Duchess' war-torn world (the Blinking World), gather info, consult with royalty, and elicit the Empress' sympathy. After some ALLEGORICAL ruminations upon the (META-LITERARY) misfortunes of the Duke and Duchess of Newcastle, the Duchess' soul returns to her corporeal body and the Empress returns to the Blazing World; they stay in immaterial touch (soul-traveling) and remain the epitome of "Platonick Friendship."]

The Second Part of the Description of the New Blazing-World

The Empress having now ordered and setled her Government to the best advantage and quiet of her Blazing-World, lived and reigned most happily and blessedly, and received oftentimes Visits from the Immaterial Spirits, who gave her Intelligence of all such things as she desired to know, and they were able to inform her of: One time they told her, how the World she came from, was imbroiled in a great War, and that most parts or Nations thereof made War against that Kingdom which was her Native Country, where all her Friends and Relations did live; at which the Empress was extreamly troubled; insomuch that the Emperor perceived her grief by her tears, and examining the cause thereof, she told him that she had received Intelligence from the Spirits, that that part of the World she came from, which was her native Country, was like to be destroyed by numerous Enemies that made War against it. The Emperor being very sensible of this ill news, especially of the Trouble it caused to the Empress, endeavoured to comfort her as much as possibly he could; and told her, that she might have all the assistance which the Blazing-World was able to afford. she answered, That if there were any possibility of transporting Forces out of the Blazing-World, into the World she came from, she would not fear so much the ruin thereof: but, said she, there being no probability of effecting anysuch thing, I know not how to shew my readiness to serve my Native Country. The Emperor asked, Whether those Spirits that gave her Intelligence of this War, could not with all their Power and Forces, assist her against those Enemies? she answered, That Spirits could not arm themselves, nor make any use of Artificial Arms or Weapons; for their Vehicles were Natural Bodies, not Artificial: Besides, said she, the violent and strong actions of war, will never agree with Immaterial Spirits; for Immaterial Spirits cannot fight, nor make Trenches, Fortifications, and the like. But, said the Emperor, their Vehicles can; especially if those Vehicles be mens Bodies, they may be serviceable in all the actions of War. Alas, replied the Empress, that will never do; for first, said she, it will be difficult to get so many dead Bodies for their Vehicles, as to make up a whole Army, much more to make many Armies to fight with so many several Nations; nay, if this could be, yet it is not possible to get so many dead and undissolved Bodies in one Nation; and for transporting them out of other Nations, it would be a thing of great difficulty and improbability: But put the case, said she, all these difficulties could be overcome; yet there is one obstruction or hindrance which can no ways be avoided: For although those dead and undissolved Bodies did all die in one minute of time; yet before they could Rendezvouze, and be put into a posture of War, to make a great and formidable Army, they would stink and dissolve; and when they came to a fight, they would moulder into dust and ashes, and so leave the purer Immaterial Spirits naked: nay, were it also possible, that those dead bodies could be preserved from stinking and dissolving, yet the Souls of such Bodies would not suffer Immaterial Spirits to rule and order them, but they would enter and govern them themselves, as being the right owners thereof, which would produce a War between those Immaterial Souls, and the Immaterial Spirits in Material Bodies; all which would hinder them from doing any service in the actions of War, against the Enemies of my Native Countrey. You speak Reason, said the Emperor, and I wish with all my Soul I could advise any manner or way, that you might be able to assist it; but you having told me of your dear Platonick Friend the Duchess of Newcastle and of her good and profitable Counsels, I would desire you to send for her Soul, and conferr with her about this business.

The Empress was very glad of this motion of the Emperor, and immediately sent for the Soul of the said Duchess, which in a minute waited on her Majesty. Then the Empress declared to her the grievance and sadness of her mind, and how much she was troubled and afflicted at the News brought her by the Immaterial Spirits, desiring the Duchess, if possible, to assist her with the best Counsels she could, that she might shew the greatness of her love and affection which she bore to her Native Countrey. Whereupon the Duchess promised her Majesty to do what lay in her power; and since it was a business of great Importance, she desired some time to consider of it; for, said she, Great Affairs require deep Considerations; which the

Empress willingly allowed her. And after the Duchess had considered some little time, she desired the Empress to send some of her Syrens or Mear men, to see what passages they could find out of the Blazing-World, into the World she came from; for, said she, if there be a passage for a Ship to come out of that World into this; then certainly there may also a Ship pass thorow the same passage out of this World into that. Hereupon the Mear- or Fish-men were sent out; who being many in number, employ'd all their industry, and did swim several ways; at last having found out the passage, they returned to the Empress, and told her, That as their Blazing World had but one Emperor, one Government, one Religion, and one Language, so there was but one Passage into that World, which was so little, that no Vessel bigger than a Packet-Boat could go thorow; neither was that Passage always open, but sometimes quite frozen up. At which Relation both the Empress and Duchess seemed somewhat troubled, fearing that this would perhaps be an hindrance or obstruction to their Design.

At last the Duchess desired the Empress to send for her Ship-wrights, and all her Architects, which were Giants; who being called, the Duchess told them how some in her own World had been so ingenious, as to contrive Ships that could swim under Water, and asked, Whether they could do the like? The Giants answered, They had never heard of that Invention; nevertheless, they would try what might be done by Art, and spare no labour or industry to find it out. In the mean time, while both the Empress and Duchess were in a serious Counsel, after many debates, the Duchess desired but a few Ships to transport some of the Bird- Worm- and Bear-men: Alas! said the Empress, What can such sorts of Men do in the other World? especially so few? They will be soon destroyed, for a Musket will destroy numbers of Birds in one shot. The Duchess said, I desire your Majesty will have but a little patience, and relie upon my advice, and you shall not fail to save your own Native Country, and in a manner become a Mistress of all that World you came from. The Empress, who loved the Duchess as her own Soul, did so; the Giants returned soon after, and told her Majesty, that they had found out the Art which the Duchess had mentioned, to make such Ships as could swim under water; which the Empress and Duchess were both very glad at, and when the Ships were made ready, the Duchess told the Empress, that it was requisite that her Majesty should go her self in body, as well as in Soul; but I, said she, can onely wait on your Majesty after a Spiritual manner, that is, with my Soul. Your Soul, said the Empress, shall live with my Soul, in my Body; for I shall onely desire your Counsel and Advice. Then said the Duchess, Your Majesty must command a great number of your Fish-men to wait on your Ships; for you know that your Ships are not made for Cannons, and therefore are no ways serviceable in War; for though by the help of your Engines, they can drive on, and your Fish-men may by the help of Chains and Ropes, draw them which way they will, to make them go on, or flye back, yet not so as to fight: And though your Ships be of Gold, and cannot be shot thorow, but onely bruised and battered; yet the Enemy will assault and enter them, and take them as Prizes; wherefore your Fishmen must do you Service instead of Cannons. But how, said the Empress, can the Fish-men do me service against an Enemy, without Cannons and all sorts of Arms? That is the reason, answered the Duchess, that I would have numbers of Fish-men, for they shall destroy all your Enemies Ships, before they can come near you. The Empress asked in what manner that could be? Thus, answered the Duchess: Your Majesty must send a number of Worm-men to the Burning-Mountains (for you have good store of them in the Blazing-World) which must get a great quantity of the Fire-stone, whose property, you know, is, that it burns so long as it is wet; and the Ships in the other World being all made of Wood, they may by that means set them all on fire; and if you can but destroy their Ships, and hinder their Navigation, you will be Mistress of all that World, by reason most parts thereof cannot live without Navigation. Besides, said she, the Fire-stone will serve you instead of Light or Torches; for you know, that the World you are going into, is dark at nights (especially if there be no Moon-shine, or if the Moon be overshadowed by Clouds) and not so full of Blazing-Stars as this World is, which make as great a light in the absence of the Sun, as the Sun doth when it is present; for that World hath but little blinking Stars, which make more shadows then light, and are onely able to draw up Vapours from the Earth, but not to rarifie or clarifie them, or to convert them into serene air.

This Advice of the Duchess was very much approved; and joyfully embraced by the Empress, who forthwith sent her Worm-men to get a good quantity of the mentioned Fire-stone. she also commanded numbers of Fish-men to wait on her under Water, and Bird-men to wait on her in the Air; and Bear- and Worm-men to wait on her in Ships, according to the Duchess's advice; and indeed the Bear-men were as serviceable to her, as the North Star; but the Bird-men would often rest themselves upon the Deck of the Ships; neither would the Empress, being of a sweet and noble Nature, suffer that they should tire or weary themselves by long flights; for though by Land they did often fly out of one Countrey into another, yet they did rest in some Woods, or on some Grounds, especially at night, when it was their sleeping time: And therefore the Empress was forced to take a great many Ships along with her, both for transporting those several sorts of her loyal and serviceable Subjects, and to carry provisions for them: Besides, she was so wearied with the Petitions of several others of her Subjects who desired to wait on her Majesty, that she could not possibly deny them all; for some would rather chuse to be drowned, then not tender their duty to her.

Thus after all things were made fit and ready, the Empress began her Journey; I cannot properly say, she set Sail, by reason in some Part, as in the passage between the two Worlds (which yet was but short) the Ships were drawn under water by the Fish-men with Golden Chains, so that they had no need of Sails there, nor of any other Arts, but onely to keep out water from entering into the Ships, and to give or make so much Air as would serve, for breath or respiration, those Land-Animals that were in the Ships; which the Giants had so Artificially contrived, that they which were therein, found no inconveniency at all: And after they had passed the Icy Sea, the Golden Ships appeared above Water, and so went on until they came near the Kingdom that was the Empress's Native Countrey; where the Bear-men through their Telescopes discovered a great number of Ships which had beset all that Kingdom, well rigg'd and mann'd.

The Empress before she came in sight of the Enemy, sent some of her Fish- and Bird-men to bring her intelligence of their Fleet; and hearing of their number, their station and posture, she gave order that when it was Night, her Bird-men should carry in their beeks some of the mentioned Fire-stones, with the tops thereof wetted; and the Fish-men should carry them likewise, and hold them out of the Water; for they were cut in the form of Torches or Candles, and being many thousands, made a terrible shew; for it appear'd as if all the Air and Sea had been of a Flaming-Fire; and all that were upon the Sea, or near it, did verily believe, the time of Judgment, or the Last Day was come, which made them all fall down, and Pray.

At the break of Day, the Empress commanded those Lights to be put out, and then the Naval Forces of the Enemy perceived nothing but a Number of Ships without Sails, Guns, Arms, and other Instruments of War; which Ships seemed to swim of themselves, without any help or assistance: which sight put them into a great amaze; neither could they perceive that those Ships were of Gold, by reason the Empress had caused them all to be coloured black, or with a dark colour; so that the natural colour of the Gold could not be perceived through the artificial colour of the paint, no not by the best Telescopes. All which put the Enemies Fleet into such a fright at night, and to such wonder in the morning, or at day-time, that they know not what to judg or make of them; for they know neither what Ships they were, nor what Party they belonged to, insomuch that they had no power to stir.

In the mean while, the Empress knowing the Colours of her own Country, sent a Letter to their General, and the rest of the chief Commanders, to let them know, that she was a great and powerful Princess, and came to assist them against their Enemies: wherefore she desired they should declare themselves, when they would have her help and assistance.

Hereupon a Councel was called, and the business debated; but there were so many cross and different Opinions, that they could not suddenly resolve what answer to send the Empress; at which she grew angry, insomuch that she resolved to return into her Blazing- World, without giving any assistance to her Countrymen: but the Duchess of Newcastle intreated her Majesty to abate her passion; for, said she, Great Councels are most commonly slow, because many men have many several Opinions: besides, every Councellor striving to be the wisest, makes long speeches, and raise many doubts, which cause retardments. If I had long-speeched Councellors, replied the Empress, I would hang them, by reason they give more Words, then Advice. The Duchess answered, That her Majesty should not be angry, but consider the differences of that and her Blazing-World; for, said she, they are not both alike; but there are grosser and duller understandings in this, than in the Blazing-World.

At last a Messenger came out, who returned the Empress thanks for her kind proffer, but desired withal, to know from whence she came, and how, and in what manner her assistance could be serviceable to them? The Empress answered, That she was not bound to tell them whence she came; but as for the manner of her assistance, I will appear, said she, to your Navy in a splendorous Light, surrounded with Fire. The Messenger asked at what time they should expect her coming? I'le be with you, answered the Empress, about one of the Clock at night. With this report the Messenger returned; which made both the poor Councellors and Sea-men much afraid; but yet they longed for the time to behold this strange sight.

The appointed hour being come, the Empress appear'd with Garments made of the Star-stone, and was born or supported above the Water, upon the Fish- mens heads and backs, so that she seemed to walk upon the face of the Water, and the Bird- and Fish-men carried the Fire-stone, lighted both in the Air, and above the Waters.

Which sight, when her Country-men perceived at a distance, their hearts began to tremble; but coming something nearer, she left her Torches, and appeared onely in her Garments of Light, like an Angel, or some Deity, and all kneeled down before her, and worshipped her with all submission and reverence: But the Empress would not come nearer than at such a distance where her voice might be generally heard, by reason she would not have that any of her Accoustrements should be perceived, but the splendor thereof; and when she was come so near that her voice could be heard and understood by all, she made this following Speech:

Dear Country-men, for so you are, although you know me not; I being a Native of this Kingdom, and hearing that most part of this World had resolved to make Warr against it, and sought to destroy it, at least to weaken its Naval Force and Power, have made a Voyage out of another World, to lend you my assistance against your Enemies. I come not to make bargains with you, or to regard my own Interest more than your Safety; but I intend to make you the most powerful Nation of this World, and therefore I have chosen rather to quit my own Tranquility, Riches and Pleasure, than suffer you to be ruined and destroyed. All the Return I desire, is but your grateful acknowledgment, and to declare my Power, Love and Loyalty to my Native Country: for, although I am now a Great and Absolute Princess, and Empress of a whole World, yet I acknowledg, that once I was a Subject of this Kingdom, which is but a small part of this World; and therefore I will have you undoubtedly believe, that I shall destroy all your Enemies before this following Night, I mean those which trouble you by Sea; and if you have any by Land, assure your self I shall also give you my assistance against them, and make you triumph over all that seek your Ruine and Destruction.

Upon this Declaration of the Empress, when both the General, and all the Commanders in their several Ships, had return'd their humble and hearty Thanks to Her Majesty for so great a favour to them, she took her leave, and departed to her own Ships. But, good Lord! what several Opinions and Judgments did this produce in the minds of her Country-men! some said she was an Angel; others, she was a sorceress; some believed her a Goddess; others said the Devil deluded them in the shape of a fine Lady.

The morning after, when the Navies were to fight, the Empress appear'd upon the face of the Waters, dress'd in her Imperial Robes, which were all of Diamonds and Carbuncles; in one hand she held a Buckler, made of one intire Carbuncle; and in the other hand a Spear of one intire Diamond; on her head she had a Cap of Diamonds, and just upon the top of the Crown, was a Starr made of the Starr-stone, mentioned heretofore; and a Half-Moon made of the same Stone, was placed on her forehead; all her other Garments were of several sorts of precious Jewels; and having given her Fish-men directions how to destroy the Enemies of her Native Country, she proceeded to effect her design. The Fish-men were to carry the Fire-stones in cases of Diamonds (for the Diamonds in the Blazing-World, are in splendor so far beyond the Diamonds of this World, as Peble-stones are to the best sort of this Worlds Diamonds) and to uncase or uncover those Fire-stones no sooner but when they were just under the Enemis Ships, or close at their sides, and then to wet them, and set their Ships on fire; which was no sooner done, but all the Enemie's Fleet was of a Flaming fire; and coming to the place where the Powder was, it streight blew them up; so that all the several Navies of the Enemies, were destroyed in a short time: which when her Countrymen did see, they all cried out with one voice, That she was an Angel sent from God to deliver them out of the hands of their Enemies: Neither would she return into the Blazing-World, until she had forced all the rest of the World to submit to that same Nation.

In the mean time, the General of all their Naval Forces, sent to their soveraign to acquaint him with their miraculous Delivery and Conquest, and with the Empress's design of making him the most powerful Monarch of all that World. After a short time, the Empress sent her self, to the soveraign of that Nation to know in what she could be serviceable to him; who returning her many thanks, both for her assistance against his Enemies, and her kind proffer to do him further service for the good and benefit of his Nations (for he was King over several Kingdoms) sent her word, that although she did partly destroy his Enemies by Sea, yet, they were so powerful, that they did hinder the Trade and Traffick of his Dominions. To which the Empress returned this answer, That she would burn and sink all those Ships that would not pay him Tribute; and forthwith sent to all the Neighbouring Nations, who had any Traffick by Sea, desiring them to pay Tribute to the King and soveraign of that Nation where she was born; But they denied it with great scorn. Whereupon, she immediately commanded her Fish-men, to destroy all strangers Ships that traffick'd on the Seas; which they did according to the Empress's Command; and when the Neighbouring Nations and Kingdoms perceived her power, they were so discomposed in their affairs and designs, that they knew not what to do: At last they sent to the Empress, and desired to treat with her, but could get no other conditions then to submit and pay Tribute to the said King and soveraign of her Native Country, otherwise, she was resolved to ruin all their Trade and Traffick by burning their Ships. Long was this Treaty, but in fine, they could obtain nothing, so that at last they were inforced to submit; by which the King of the mentioned Nations became absolute Master of the Seas, and consequently of that World; by reason, as I mentioned heretofore, the several Nations of that World could not well live without Traffick and Commerce, by Sea, as well as by Land.

But after a short time, those Neighbouring Nations finding themselves so much inslaved, that they were hardly able to peep out of their own

Dominions without a chargeable Tribute, they all agreed to join again their Forces against the King and soveraign of the said Dominions; which when the Empress receiv'd notice of, she sent out her Fish-men to destroy, as they had done before, the remainder of all their Naval Power, by which they were soon forced again to submit, except some Nations which could live without Foreign Traffick, and some whose Trade and Traffick was meerly by Land; these would no ways be Tributary to the mentioned King. The Empress sent them word, That in case they did not submit to him, she intended to fire all their Towns and Cities, and reduce them by force, to what they would not yield with a good will. But they rejected and scorned her Majesties Message, which provoked her anger so much, that she resolved to send her Bird- and Worm men thither, with order to begin first with their smaller Towns, and set them on fire (for she was loath to make more spoil then she was forced to do) and if they remain'd still obstinate in their resolutions, to destroy also their greater Cities. The onely difficulty was, how to convey the Worm-men conveniently to those places; but they desired that her Majesty would but set them upon any part of the Earth of those Nations, and they could travel within the Earth as easily, and as nimbly as men upon the face of the Earth; which the Empress did according to their desire.

But before both the Bird- and Worm-men began their journey, the Empress commanded the Bearmen to view through their Telescopes what Towns and Cities those were that would not submit; and having a full information thereof, she instructed the Bird- and Bear-men what Towns they should begin withal; in the mean while she sent to all the Princes and soveraigns of those Nations, to let them know that she would give them a proof of her Power, and check their Obstinacies by burning some of their smaller Towns; and if they continued still in their Obstinate Resolutions, that she would convert their smaller Loss into a Total Ruin. she also commanded her Bird-men to make their flight at night, lest they be perceived. At last when both the Bird- and Worm-men came to the designed places, the Worm-men laid some Fire-stones under the Foundation of every House, and the Bird-men placed some at the tops of them, so that both by rain, and by some other moisture within the Earth, the stones could not fail of burning. The Bird-men in the mean time having learned some few words of their Language, told them, That the next time it did rain, their Towns would be all on fire; at which they were amaz'd to hear Men speak in the air; but withall they laughed when they heard them say that rain should fire their Towns; knowing that the effect of Water was to quench, not produce Fire.

At last a rain came, and upon a sudden all their Houses appeared of a flaming Fire; and the more Water there was poured on them, the more they did flame and burn; which struck such a Fright and Terror into all the Neighbouring Cities, Nations and Kingdoms, that for fear the like should happen to them, they and all the rest of the parts of that World, granted the Empress's desire, and submitted to the Monarch and sovereign of her Native Countrey, the King of Esfi; save one, which having seldom or never any rain, but onely dews, which would soon be spent in a great fire, slighted her Power: The Empress being desirous to make it stoop as well as the rest, knew that every year it was watered by a flowing Tide, which lasted some Weeks; and although their Houses stood high from the ground, yet they were built upon Supporters which were fixt into the ground. Wherefore she commanded both her Bird- and Worm-men to lay some of the Fire-stones at the bottom of those Supporters, and when the Tide came in, all their Houses were of a Fire, which did so rarifie the Water, that the Tide was soon turn'd into a Vapour, and this Vapour again into Air; which caused not onely a destruction of their Houses, but also a general barrenness over all their Countrey that year, and forced them to submit, as well as the rest of the World had done.

Thus the Empress did not onely save her Native Country, but made it the Absolute Monarchy of all that World; and both the effects of her Power and her Beauty, did kindle a great desire in all the greatest Princes to see her; who hearing that she was resolved to return into her own Blazing-World, they all entreated the favour, that they might wait on her Majesty before she went. The Empress sent word, That she should be glad to grant their Requests; but having no other place of Reception for them, she desired that they would be pleased to come into the open Seas with their Ships, and make a Circle of a pretty large compass, and then her own Ships should meet them, and close up the Circle, and she would present her self to the view of all those that came to see her: Which Answer was joyfully received by all the mentioned Princes, who came, some sooner, and some later, each according to the distance of his Countrey, and the length of the voyage. And being all met in the form and manner aforesaid, the Empress appeared upon the face of the Water in her Imperial Robes; in some part of her hair, near her face, she had placed some of the Starr- Stone, which added such a luster and glory to it, that it caused a great admiration in all that were present, who believed her to be some Celestial Creature, or rather an uncreated Goddess, and they all had a desire to worship her; for surely, said they, no mortal creature can have such a splendid and transcendent beauty, nor can any have so great a power as she has, to walk upon the Waters, and to destroy whatever she pleases, not onely whole Nations, but a whole World.

The Empress expressed to her own Countrymen, who were also her Interpreters to the rest of the Princes that were present, That she would give them an Entertainment at the darkest time of Night: Which being come, the Fire-Stones were lighted, which made both Air and Seas appear of a bright shining flame, insomuch that they put all Spectators into an extream fright, who verily believed they should all be destroyed; which the Empress perceiving, caused all the Lights of the Fire-Stones to be put out, and onely shewed her self in her Garments of Light. The Bird-men carried her upon their backs into the Air, and there she appear'd as glorious as the Sun. Then she was set down upon the Seas again, and presently there was heard the most melodious and sweetest Consort of Voices, as ever was heard out of the Seas, which was made by the Fish- men; this Consort was answered by another, made by the Bird-men in the Air, so that it seem'd as if Sea and Air had spoke, and answered each other by way of Singing-Dialogues, or after the manner of those Playes that are acted by singing-Voices.

But when it was upon break of day, the Empress ended her Entertainment, and at full day-light all the Princes perceived that she went into the Ship wherein the Prince and Monarch of her Native Country was, the King of Esfi, with whom she had several Conferences; and having assured Him of the readiness of her Assistance whensoever he required it, telling Him withal, That she wanted no Intelligence, she went forth again upon the Waters, and being in the midst of the Circle made by those Ships that were present, she desired them to draw somewhat nearer, that they might hear her speak; which being done, she declared her self in this following manner:

Great, Heroick, and Famous Monarchs, I come hither to assist the King of Esfi against his Enemies, He being unjustly assaulted by many several Nations, which would fain take away His Hereditary Rights, and Prerogatives of the Narrow Seas; at which Unjustice, Heaven was much displeased, and for the Injuries He received from His Enemies, rewarded Him with an Absolute Power, so that now he is become the Head-Monarch of all this World; which Power, though you may envy, yet you can no wayes hinder Him; for all those that endeavour to resist His Power, shall onely get Loss for their Labour, and no Victory for their Profit. Wherefore my advice to you all is, To pay him Tribute justly and truly, that you may live Peaceably and Happily, and be rewarded with the Blessings of Heaven: which I wish you from my Soul.

After the Empress had thus finished her Speech to the Princes of the several Nations of that World, she desired that in their Ships might fall back; which being done, her own Fleet came into the Circle, without any visible assistance of Sails or Tide; and her self being entred into her own Ship, the whole Fleet sunk immediately into the bottom of the Seas, and left all the Spectators in a deep amazement; neither would she suffer any of her Ships to come above the Waters, until she arrived into the Blazing-World.

In time of the Voyage, both the Empress's and the Duchess's Soul, were very gay and merry; and sometimes they would converse very seriously with each other. Amongst the rest of their discourses, the Duchess said, she wondred much at one thing, which was, That since her Majesty had found out a passage out of the Blazing-World, into the World she came from, she did not enrich that part of the World where she was born, at least her own Family, though she had enough to enrich the whole World. The Empress's Soul answered, That she loved her Native Countrey, and her own Family, as well as any Creature could do; and that this was the reason why she would not enrich them: for, said she, not only particular Families or Nations, but all the World, their Natures are such, that much Gold, and great store of Riches, makes them mad; insomuch as they endeavour to destroy each other for Gold or Riches sake. The reason thereof is, said the Duchess, that they have too little Gold and Riches, which makes them so eager to have it. No, replied the Empress's Soul, their particular Covetousness, is beyond all the wealth of the richest World, and the more Riches they have, the more Covetous they are; for their Covetousness is Infinite. But, said she, I would there could a Passage be found out of the Blazing-World, into the World whence you came, and I would willingly give you as much Riches as you desir'd. The Duchess's Soul gave her Majesty humble thanks for her great Favour; and told her, that she was not covetous, nor desir'd any more wealth than what her Lord and Husband had before the Civil-Warrs. Neither, said she, should I desire it for my own, but my Lord's Posterities sake. Well, said the Empress, I'le command my Fish-men to use all their Skill and Industry to find out a Passage into that World which your Lord and Husband is in. I do verily believe, answered the Duchess, that there will be no Passage found into that World; but if there were any, I should not Petition your Majesty for Gold and Jewels, but only for the Elixir that grows in the midst of the Golden Sands, for to preserve Life and Health; but without a Passage, it is impossible to carry away any of it: for, whatsoever is Material, cannot travel like Immaterial Beings, such as Souls and Spirits are. Neither do Souls require any such thing that might revive them, or prolong their Lives, by reason they are unalterable: for, were Souls like Bodies, then my Soul might have had the benefit of that Natural Elixir that grows in your Blazing-World. I wish earnestly, said the

Empress, that a Passage might be found, and then both your Lord and your self, should neither want Wealth, nor Long-life: nay, I love you so well, that I would make you as Great and Powerful a Monarchess, as I am of the Blazing-World. The Duchess's Soul humbly thank'd her Majesty, and told her, That she acknowledged and esteemed her Love beyond all things that are in Nature.

After this Discourse, they had many other Conferences, which for brevity's sake I'le forbear to rehearse. At last, after several Questions which the Empress's Soul asked the Duchess, she desired to know the reason why she did take such delight, when she was joyned to her Body, in being singular both in Accoustrements, Behaviour, and Discourse? The Duchess's Soul answered, she confessed that it was extravagant, and beyond what was usual and ordinary: but yet her ambition being such, that she would not be like others in any thing, if it were possible, I endeavour, said she, to be as singular as I can: for, it argues but a mean Nature, to imitate others: and though I do not love to be imitated, if I can possibly avoid it; yet, rather than imitate others, I should chuse to be imitated by others: for my Nature is such, that I had rather appear worse in Singularity, than better in the Mode. If you were not a great Lady, replied the Empress, you would never pass in the World for a wise Lady: for, the World would say, your Singularities are Vanities. The Duchess's Soul answered, she did not at all regard the Censure of this, or any other Age, concerning Vanities: but, said she, neither this present, nor any of the future Ages, can or will truly say, that I am not Vertuous and Chast: for I am confident, all that were, or are acquainted with me, and all the Servants which ever I had, will or can upon their oaths declare my actions no otherwise than Vertuous: and certainly, there's none even of the meanest Degree, which have not their Spies and Witnesses, much more those of the Nobler sort, which seldom or never are without Attendants; so that their Faults (if they have any) will easily be known, and as easily be divulged. Wherefore, happy are those Natures that are Honest, Vertuous, and Noble; not only happy to themselves, but happy to their Families. But, said the Empress, if you glory so much in your Honesty and Vertue, how comes it that you plead for Dishonest and Wicked persons, in your Writings? The Duchess answered, It was only to shew her Wit, not her Nature.

At last the Empress arrived into the Blazing-world, and coming to her Imperial Palace, you may sooner imagine than expect that I should express the joy which the Emperor had at her safe return; for he loved her beyond his Soul; and there was no love lost, for the Empress equal'd his Affection with no less love to him. After the time of rejoicing with each other, the Duchess's Soul begg'd leave to return to her Noble Lord: But the Emperor

desired, that before she departed, she would see how he had employed
his time in the Empress's absence; for he had built Stables and Riding-
Houses, and desired to have Horses of Manage, such as, according to the
Empress's Relation, the Duke of Newcastlehad: The Emperor enquired of
the Duchess, the Form and Structure of her Lord and Husband's Stables
and Riding-House. The Duchess answer'd his Majesty, That they were
but plain and ordinary; but, said she, had my Lord Wealth, I am sure he
would not spare it, in rendring his Buildings as Noble as could be made.
Hereupon the Emperor shewed the Duchess the Stables he had built, which
were most stately and magnificent; among the rest, there was one double
Stable that held a Hundred Horses on a side, the main Building was of
Gold, lined with several sorts of precious Materials; the Roof was Arched
with Agats, the sides of the Walls were lined with Cornelian, the Floor was
paved with Amber, the Mangers were Mother of Pearl; the Pillars, as also
the middle Isle or Walk of the Stables, were of Crystal; the Front and Gate
was of Turquois, most neatly cut and carved. The Riding-House was lined
with Saphirs, Topases, and the like; the Floor was all of Golden-Sand so
finely sifted, that it was extreamly soft, and not in the least hurtful to the
Horses feet, and the Door and Frontispiece was of Emeralds curiously
carved.

After the view of these Glorious and Magnificent Buildings, which the
Duchess's Soul was much delighted withall, she resolved to take her leave;
but the Emperor desired her to stay yet some short time more, for they
both loved her company so well, that they were unwilling to have her
depart so soon: several Conferences and Discourses pass'd between them;
amongst the rest, the Emperor desir'd her advice how to set up a Theatre
for Plays. The Duchess confessed her Ignorance in this Art, telling his
Majesty that she knew nothing of erecting Theatres or Scenes, but what
she had by an Immaterial Observation, when she was with the Empress's
Soul in the chief City of E. Entring into one of their Theatres, whereof
the Empress could give as much account to his Majesty, as her self. But
both the Emperor and the Empress told the Duchess, That she could give
directions how to make Plays. The Duchess answered, That she had as
little skill to form a Play after the Mode, as she had to paint or make
a Scene for shew. But you have made Plays, replied the Empress: Yes,
answered the Duchess, I intended them for Plays; but the Wits of these
present times condemned them as uncapable of being represented or acted,
because they were not made up according to the Rules of Art; though I
dare say, That the Descriptions are as good as any they have writ. The
Emperor asked, Whether the Property of Plays were not to describe the
several Humours, Actions and Fortunes of Mankind? 'Tis so, answered the

Duchess. Why then, replied the Emperor, the natural Humours, Actions and Fortunes of Mankind, are not done by the Rules of Art: But, said the Duchess, it is the Art and Method of our Wits to despise all Descriptions of Wit, Humour, Actions and Fortunes that are without such Artificial Rules. The Emperor asked, Are those good Plays that are made so Methodically and Artificially? The Duchess answer'd, They were Good according to the Judgment of the Age, or Mode of the Nation, but not according to her Judgment: for truly, said she, in my Opinion, their Plays will prove a Nursery of whining Lovers, and not an Academy or School for Wise, Witty, Noble and well-behaved men. But I, replied the Emperor, desire such a Theatre as may make wise Men; and will have such Descriptions as are Natural, not Artificial. If your Majesty be of that Opinion, said the Duchess's Soul, then my Playes may be acted in your Blazing- World, when they cannot be acted in the Blinking-World of Wit; and the next time I come to visit your Majesty, I shall endeavour to order your Majesty's Theatre, to present such Playes as my Wit is capable to make. Then the Empress told the Duchess, That she loved a foolish Farse added to a wise Play. The Duchess answered, That no World in Nature had fitter Creatures for it than the Blazing-World: for, said she, the Lowse- men, the Bird-men, the Spider- and Fox-men, the Ape-men and Satyrs appear in a Farse extraordinary pleasant.

Hereupon both the Emperor and Empress intreated the Duchess's Soul to stay so long with them, till she had ordered her Theatre, and made Playes and Farses fit for them; for they onely wanted that sort of Recreation: but the Duchess's Soul begg'd their Majesties to give her leave to go into her Native World; for she long'd to be with her dear Lord and Husband, promising, that after a short time she would return again. Which being granted, though with much difficulty, she took her leave with all Civility and Respect, and so departed from their Majesties.

After the Duchess's return into her own body, she entertained her Lord (when he was pleased to hear such kind of Discourses) with Foreign Relations; but he was never displeased to hear of the Empress's kind Commendations, and of the Characters she was pleased to give of him to the Emperor. Amongst other Relations, she told him all what had past between the Empress, and the several Monarchs of that World whither she went with the Empress; and how she had subdued them to pay Tribute and Homage to the Monarch of that Nation or Kingdom to which she owed both her Birth and Education. she also related to her Lord what Magnificent Stables and Riding-Houses the Emperor had built, and what fine Horses were in the Blazing-world, of several shapes and sizes, and how exact their shapes were in each sort, and of many various Colours, and fine Marks, as if they had been painted by Art, with such Coats or Skins, that they had a far greater gloss and smoothness than Satin; and were there but a passage out of the Blazingworld into this, said she, you should not onely have some of those Horses, but such Materials as the Emperor has, to build your Stables and Riding-Houses withall; and so much Gold, that I should never repine at your Noble and Generous Gifts. The Duke smilingly answered her, That he was sorry there was no Passage between those two Worlds; but, said he, I have always found an Obstruction to my Good Fortunes.

One time the Duchess chanced to discourse with some of her acquaintance, of the Empress of the Blazing-world, who asked her what Pastimes and Recreations her Majesty did most delight in? The Duchess answered, That she spent most of her time in the study of Natural Causes and Effects, which was her chief delight and pastime; and that she loved to discourse sometimes with the most Learned persons of that World: And to please the Emperor and his Nobles, who were all of the Royal Race, she went often abroad to take the air, but seldom in the day-time, always at night, if it might be called Night; for, said she, the Nights there, are as light as Days, by reason of the numerous Blazing-Starrs, which are very splendorous, onely their Light is whiter than the Sun's Light; and as the Sun's Light is hot, so their Light is cool; not so cool as our twinkling Starr-light, nor is their Sun-light so hot as ours, but more rate: And that part of the Blazing-world where the Empress resides, is always clear, and never subject to any Storms, Tempests, Fogs or Mists, but has onely refreshing-Dews that nourish the Earth: The air of it is sweet and temperate, and, as I said before, as much light in the Sun's absence, as in its presence, which makes that time we call Night, more pleasant there than the Day: And sometimes the Empress goes abroad by Water in Barges, sometimes by Land in Chariots, and sometimes on Horse-back; her RoyalChariots are very Glorious, the Body is one intire green Diamond; the four small Pillars that bear up the Top-cover, are four white Diamonds, cut in the form thereof; the top or roof of the Chariot, is one intire blew Diamond, and at the four corners are great springs of Rubies; the Seat is made of Cloth of Gold, stuffed with Ambergreece beaten small: the Chariot is drawn by Twelve Unicorns, whose Trappings are all Chains of Pearl; and as for her Barges, they are onely of Gold. Her Guard of State (for she needs none for security, there being no Rebels or Enemies) consists of Giants, but they seldom wait on their Majesties abroad, because their extraordinary height and bigness does hinder their prospect. Her Entertainment when she is upon the Water, is the Musick of the Fish- and Bird-men; and by Land are Horse and Foot-matches; for the Empress takes much delight in making Race-matches with the Emperor, and the Nobility; some Races are between the Fox-

and Ape-men, which sometimes the Satyrs strive to outrun; and some are between the Spider-men and Licemen. Also there are several Flight-matches, between the several sorts of Bird-men, and the several sorts of Fly-men; and swimming-matches, between the several sorts of Fish-men. The Emperor, Empress, and their Nobles, take also great delight to have Collations; for in the Blazing-world, there are most delicious Fruits of all sorts, and some such as in thisWorld were never seen nor tasted; for there are most tempting sorts of Fruit: After their Collations are ended, they Dance; and if they be upon the Water, they dance upon the Water, there lying so many Fish-men so close and thick together, as they can dance very evenly and easily upon their backs, and need not fear drowning. Their Musick, both Vocal and Instrumental, is according to their several places: Upon the Water, it is of Water-Instruments, as shells filled with Water, and so moved by Art, which is a very sweet and delightful harmony; and those Dances which they dance upon the Water, are, for the most part, such as we in this World call swimming- Dances, where they do not lift up their feet high: In Lawns, or upon Plains, they have Wind-Instruments, but much better than those in our World: And when they dance in the Woods, they have Horn-Instruments, which although they are of a sort of Wind-Instruments, yet they are of another Fashion than the former: In their Houses they have such Instruments as are somewhat like our Viols, Violins, Theorboes, Lutes, Citherins, Gittars, Harpsichords, and the like; but yet so far beyond them, that the difference cannot well be exprest; and as their places of Dancing, and their Musick is different, so is their manner or way of Dancing. In these and the like Recreations, the Emperor, Empress, and the Nobility pass their time.

The Epilogue to the Reader

By this Poetical Description, you may perceive, that my ambition is not onely to be Empress, but Authoress of a whole World; and that the Worlds I have made, both the Blazing- and the other Philosophical World, mentioned in the first part of this Description, are framed and composed of the most pure, that is, the Rational parts of Matter, which are the parts of my Mind; which Creation was more easily and suddenly effected, than the Conquests of the two famous Monarchs of the World. Alexander and Cesar. Neither have I made such disturbances, and caused so many dissolutions of particulars, otherwise named deaths, as they did; for I have destroyed but some few men in a little Boat, which dyed through the extremity of cold, and that by the hand of Justice, which was necessitated to punish their crime of stealing away a young and beauteous Lady. And in the formation of those Worlds, I take more delight and glory, then ever Alexander or Cesar did in conquering this terrestrial world; and though I have made my Blazing-world a Peaceable World, allowing it but one Religion, one Language, and one Government; yet could I make another World, as full of Factions, Divisions and Warrs, as this is of Peace and Tranquility; and the Rational figures of my Mind might express as much courage to fight, as Hector and Achilles had; and be as wise as Nestor, as; Eloquent as Ulysses, and be as beautiful as Hellen. But I esteeming Peace before Warr, Wit before Policy, Honesty before Beauty; instead of the figures of Alexander, Cesar, Hector, Achilles, Nestor, Ulysses, Hellen, &c. chose rather the figure of Honest Margaret Newcastle, which now I would not change for all this Terrestrial World; and if any should like the World I have made, and be willing to be my Subjects, they may imagine themselves such, and they are such, I mean in their Minds, Fancies or Imaginations; but if they cannot endure to be Subjects, they may create Worlds of their own, and Govern themselves as they please. But yet let them have a care, not to prove unjust Usurpers, and to rob me of mine: for, concerning the Philosophical-world, I am Empress of it my self; and as for the Blazing-world, it having an Empress already, who rules it with great Wisdom and Conduct, which Empress is my dear Platonick Friend; I shall never prove so unjust, treacherous and unworthy to her, as to disturb her Government, much less to depose her from her Imperial Throne, for the sake of any other, but rather chuse to create another World for another Friend.

Finis.

THE RIME OF THE ANCIENT MARINER (1817)

SAMUEL TAYLOR COLERIDGE (1772-1834)

Samuel Taylor Coleridge was a poet's poet: a writer, literary critic, theologian, and philosopher who helped define the Romantic Period and was chummy with a variety of lit folk in his lifetime, particularly William Wordsworth (but also Charles Lamb, Robert Southey, and Robert Lovell); his influence on later poets and critics remains significant: many continue to regard Hamlet *as Shakespeare's greatest play thanks to Coleridge's early criticism. He also coined the term "SUSPENSION OF DISBELIEF," which may cue the reader into his views on GOTHIC literature.*

*Coleridge was also—throughout much of his life—a sporadically miserable man, often ill, and ultimately addicted to laudanum (powdered opium suspended in brandy). Coleridge's trippiest poem—*Kubla Khan, Or A Vision in a Dream—*was, by his own admission, penned under/after a laudanum episode.* Rime *shows signs of similar influence, although such INTENTIONAL FALLACY should not discolor the reader's appreciation of the text itself.*

Admittedly, Rime of the Ancient Mariner *can be a confounding text to make sense of...but that's as should be. Coleridge is not offering pithy answers here or logical chains of events: he is certainly not offering Enlightenment Era CORRELATIONS masquerading as CAUSATIONS. Instead,* Rime *presents a world of supernatural wonders, of intentional ARCHAISMS, of METALITERARY EKPHRASIS, of emotion rather than reason: AESTHETICISM reigns. In addition to leaving its readers with a lingering GOTHIC mood, the poem also contains some of the most memorable—if sometimes imperfectly remembered—couplets in all English literature. "Water, water, everywhere..."*

Rime *has persisted in popular culture, inspiring an Iron Maiden song, a META comic-within-a-comic in* Watchmen, *and a surreal Monty Python sketch; it's also garnered METALITERARY shout-outs in* Frankenstein, Interview with the Vampire, *and Magic: The Gathering; according to at least one Classico-Medievalist, the poem spawned the entire* Pirates of the Caribbean *film series (not the amusement park ride: although that, indeed, would be an E-ticket).*

PART I

It is an ancient Mariner,
And he stoppeth one of three.
"By thy long grey beard and glittering eye,
Now wherefore stopp'st thou me?

The bridegroom's doors are opened wide,
And I am next of kin;
The guests are met, the feast is set:
May'st hear the merry din."

He holds him with his skinny hand,
"There was a ship," quoth he.
"Hold off! unhand me, grey-beard loon!"
Eftsoons his hand dropt he.

He holds him with his glittering eye—
The Wedding-Guest stood still,
And listens like a three years' child:
The Mariner hath his will.

The Wedding-Guest sat on a stone:
He cannot choose but hear;
And thus spake on that ancient man,
The bright-eyed Mariner.

"The ship was cheered, the harbor cleared,
Merrily did we drop
Below the kirk, below the hill,
Below the light-house top.

The sun came up upon the left,
Out of the sea came he!
And he shone bright, and on the right
Went down into the sea.

Higher and higher every day,
Till over the mast at noon—"
The Wedding-Guest here beat his breast,
For he heard the loud bassoon.

The bride hath paced into the hall,
Red as a rose is she;
Nodding their heads before her goes
The merry minstrelsy.

The Wedding-Guest he beat his breast,
Yet he cannot choose but hear;
And thus spake on that ancient man,
The bright-eyed Mariner.

"And now the Storm-blast came, and he
Was tyrannous and strong:
He struck with his o'ertaking wings,
And chased us south along.

With sloping masts and dipping prow,
As who pursued with yell and blow
Still treads the shadow of his foe,
And forward bends his head,
The ship drove fast, loud roared the blast,
And southward aye we fled.

And now there came both mist and snow,
And it grew wondrous cold:
And ice, mast-high, came floating by,
As green as emerald.

And through the drifts the snowy clifts
Did send a dismal sheen:
Nor shapes of men nor beasts we ken—
The ice was all between.

The ice was here, the ice was there,
The ice was all around:
It cracked and growled, and roared and howled,
Like noises in a swound!

At length did cross an Albatross,
Thorough the fog it came;
As if it had been a Christian soul,
We hailed it in God's name.

It ate the food it ne'er had eat,
And round and round it flew.
The ice did split with a thunder-fit;
The helmsman steered us through!

And a good south wind sprung up behind;
The Albatross did follow,
And every day, for food or play,
Came to the mariners' hollo!

In mist or cloud, on mast or shroud,
It perched for vespers nine;
Whiles all the night, through fog-smoke white,
Glimmered the white moon-shine."

"God save thee, ancient Mariner!
From the fiends, that plague thee thus!—
Why look'st thou so?"—"With my cross-bow
I shot the Albatross.

PART II

The Sun now rose upon the right:
Out of the sea came he,
Still hid in mist, and on the left
Went down into the sea.

And the good south wind still blew behind,
But no sweet bird did follow,
Nor any day for food or play
Came to the mariners' hollo!

And I had done a hellish thing,
And it would work 'em woe:
For all averred, I had killed the bird
That made the breeze to blow.

Ah wretch! said they, the bird to slay,
That made the breeze to blow!
Nor dim nor red, like God's own head,
The glorious Sun uprist:
Then all averred, I had killed the bird

That brought the fog and mist.

'T was right, said they, such birds to slay,
That bring the fog and mist.
The fair breeze blew, the white foam flew,
The furrow followed free;
We were the first that ever burst
Into that silent sea.

Down dropt the breeze, the sails dropt down,
'T was sad as sad could be;
And we did speak only to break
The silence of the sea!

All in a hot and copper sky,
The bloody Sun, at noon,
Right up above the mast did stand,
No bigger than the Moon.

Day after day, day after day,
We stuck, nor breath nor motion;
As idle as a painted ship
Upon a painted ocean.

Water, water, every where,
And all the boards did shrink;
Water, water, every where
Nor any drop to drink.

The very deep did rot: O Christ!
That ever this should be!
Yea, slimy things did crawl with legs
Upon the slimy sea.

About, about, in reel and rout
The death-fires danced at night;
The water, like a witch's oils,
Burnt green, and blue and white.

And some in dreams assured were
Of the Spirit that plagued us so;
Nine fathom deep he had followed us

From the land of mist and snow.

And every tongue, through utter drought,
Was withered at the root;
We could not speak, no more than if
We had been choked with soot.

Ah! well-a-day! what evil looks
Had I from old and young!
Instead of the cross, the Albatross
About my neck was hung.

PART III

There passed a weary time. Each throat
Was parched, and glazed each eye.
A weary time! a weary time!
How glazed each weary eye,
When looking westward, I beheld
A something in the sky.

At first it seemed a little speck,
And then it seemed a mist;
It moved and moved, and took at last
A certain shape, I wist.

A speck, a mist, a shape, I wist!
And still it neared and neared:
As if it dodged a water-sprite,
It plunged and tacked and veered.

With throats unslaked, with black lips baked,
We could nor laugh nor wail;
Through utter drought all dumb we stood!
I bit my arm, I sucked the blood,
And cried, A sail! a sail!

With throats unslaked, with black lips baked,
Agape they heard me call:
Gramercy! they for joy did grin,
And all at once their breath drew in,
As they were drinking all.

See! see! (I cried) she tacks no more!
Hither to work us weal;
Without a breeze, without a tide,
She steadies with upright keel!

The western wave was all a-flame.
The day was well nigh done!
Almost upon the western wave
Rested the broad bright Sun;
When that strange shape drove suddenly
Betwixt us and the Sun;

And straight the Sun was flecked with bars,
(Heaven's Mother send us grace!)
As if through a dungeon-grate he peered
With broad and burning face.

Alas (thought I, and my heart beat loud)
How fast she nears and nears!
Are those her sails that glance in the Sun,
Like restless gossameres?

Are those her ribs through which the Sun
Did peer, as through a grate?
And is that Woman all her crew?
Is that a Death? and are there two?
Is Death that woman's mate?

Her lips were red, her looks were free,
Her locks were yellow as gold:
Her skin was as white as leprosy,
The Night-mare Life-in-Death was she,
Who thicks man's blood with cold.
The naked hulk alongside came,
And the twain were casting dice;
'The game is done! I've won! I've won!'
Quoth she, and whistles thrice.

The Sun's rim dips; the stars rush out;
At one stride comes the dark;
With far-heard whisper, o'er the sea,

Off shot the spectre-bark.

We listened and looked sideways up!
Fear at my heart, as at a cup,
My life-blood seemed to sip!
The stars were dim, and thick the night,
The steersman's face by his lamp gleamed white;
From the sails the dew did drip—
Till clomb above the eastern bar
The horned Moon, with one bright star
Within the nether tip.

One after one, by the star-dogged Moon,
Too quick for groan or sigh,
Each turned his face with a ghastly pang,
And cursed me with his eye.

Four times fifty living men,
(And I heard nor sigh nor groan)
With heavy thump, a lifeless lump,
They dropped down one by one.

The souls did from their bodies fly,—
They fled to bliss or woe!
And every soul, it passed me by,
Like the whizz of my cross-bow!"

PART IV

"I Fear thee, ancient Mariner!
I fear thy skinny hand!
And thou art long, and lank, and brown,
As is the ribbed sea-sand.

I fear thee and thy glittering eye,
And thy skinny hand, so brown."—
"Fear me not, fear not, thou wedding-guest!
This body dropt not down.

Alone, alone, all, all alone,
Alone on the wide, wide sea!
And never a saint took pity on

My soul in agony.

The many men, so beautiful!
And they all dead did lie:
And a thousand thousand slimy things
Lived on; and so did I.

I looked upon the rotting sea,
And drew my eyes away;
I looked upon the rotting deck,
And there the dead men lay.

I looked to heaven, and tried to pray;
But or ever a prayer had gusht,
A wicked whisper came, and made
My heart as dry as dust.

I closed my lids, and kept them close,
And the balls like pulses beat;
For the sky and the sea, and the sea and the sky
Lay like a load on my weary eye,
And the dead were at my feet.

The cold sweat melted from their limbs,
Nor rot nor reek did they:
The look with which they looked on me
Had never passed away.

An orphan's curse would drag to hell
A spirit from on high;
But oh! more horrible than that
Is a curse in a dead man's eye!
Seven days, seven nights, I saw that curse,
And yet I could not die.

The moving Moon went up the sky,
And nowhere did abide:
Softly she was going up,
And a star or two beside—

Her beams bemocked the sultry main,
Like April hoar-frost spread;

But where the ship's huge shadow lay,
The charmed water burnt alway
A still and awful red.

Beyond the shadow of the ship,
I watched the water-snakes:
They moved in tracks of shining white,
And when they reared, the elfish light
Fell off in hoary flakes.

Within the shadow of the ship
I watched their rich attire:
Blue, glossy green, and velvet black,
They coiled and swam; and every track
Was a flash of golden fire.

O happy living things! no tongue
Their beauty might declare:
A spring of love gushed from my heart,
And I blessed them unaware:
Sure my kind saint took pity on me,
And I blessed them unaware.

The selfsame moment I could pray;
And from my neck so free
The Albatross fell off, and sank
Like lead into the sea.

PART V

Oh sleep! it is a gentle thing,
Beloved from pole to pole!
To Mary Queen the praise be given!
She sent the gentle sleep from Heaven,
That slid into my soul.

The silly buckets on the deck,
That had so long remained,
I dreamt that they were filled with dew;
And when I awoke, it rained.

My lips were wet, my throat was cold,

My garments all were dank;
Sure I had drunken in my dreams,
And still my body drank.

I moved, and could not feel my limbs:
I was so light—almost
I thought that I had died in sleep,
And was a blessed ghost.

And soon I heard a roaring wind:
It did not come anear;
But with its sound it shook the sails,
That were so thin and sere.

The upper air burst into life!
And a hundred fire-flags sheen,
To and fro they were hurried about!
And to and fro, and in and out,
The wan stars danced between.

And the coming wind did roar more loud,
And the sails did sigh like sedge;
And the rain poured down from one black cloud;
The Moon was at its edge.

The thick black cloud was cleft, and still
The Moon was at its side.
Like waters shot from some high crag,
The lightning fell with never a jag,
A river steep and wide.

The loud wind never reached the ship,
Yet now the ship moved on!
Beneath the lightning and the Moon
The dead men gave a groan.

They groaned, they stirred, they all uprose,
Nor spake, nor moved their eyes;
It had been strange, even in a dream,
To have seen those dead men rise.

The helmsman steered, the ship moved on;

Yet never a breeze up blew;
The mariners all 'gan work the ropes,
Where they were wont to do;
They raised their limbs like lifeless tools—
We were a ghastly crew.

The body of my brother's son
Stood by me, knee to knee:
The body and I pulled at one rope,
But he said nought to me."

"I fear thee, ancient Mariner!"
"Be calm, thou Wedding-Guest!
'T was not those souls that fled in pain,
Which to their corses came again,
But a troop of spirits blest:

For when it dawned—they dropped their arms,
And clustered round the mast;
Sweet sounds rose slowly through their mouths,
And from their bodies passed.

Around, around, flew each sweet sound,
Then darted to the Sun;
Slowly the sounds came back again,
Now mixed, now one by one.

Sometimes a-dropping from the sky
I heard the sky-lark sing;
Sometimes all little birds that are,
How they seemed to fill the sea and air
With their sweet jargoning!

And now 't was like all instruments,
Now like a lonely flute;
And now it is an angel's song,
That makes the heavens be mute.

It ceased; yet still the sails made on
A pleasant noise till noon,
A noise like of a hidden brook
In the leafy month of June,

That to the sleeping woods all night
Singeth a quiet tune.

Till noon we quietly sailed on,
Yet never a breeze did breathe:
Slowly and smoothly went the ship,
Moved onward from beneath.

Under' the keel nine fathom deep,
From the land of mist and snow,
The spirit slid: and it was he
That made the ship to go.
The sails at noon left off their tune,
And the ship stood still also.

The Sun, right up above the mast,
Had fixed her to the ocean:
But in a minute she 'gan stir,
With a short uneasy motion—
Backwards and forwards half her length
With a short uneasy motion.

Then like a pawing horse let go,
She made a sudden bound:
It flung the blood into my head,
And I fell down in a swound.

How long in that same fit I lay,
I have not to declare;
But ere my living life returned,
I heard and in my soul discerned
Two voices in the air.

'Is it he?' quoth one, 'Is this the man?
By him who died on cross,
With his cruel bow he laid full low
The harmless Albatross.

The spirit who bideth by himself
In the land of mist and snow,
He loved the bird that loved the man
Who shot him with his bow?'

The other was a softer voice,
As soft as honey-dew:
Quoth he, 'The man hath penance done,
And penance more will do.'

PART VI

FIRST VOICE
'But tell me, tell me! speak again,
Thy soft response renewing—
What makes that ship drive on so fast?
What is the ocean doing?'

SECOND VOICE
'Still as a slave before his lord,
The ocean hath no blast;
His great bright eye most silently
Up to the Moon is cast—

If he may know which way to go;
For she guides him smooth or grim.
See, brother, see! how graciously
She looketh down on him.'

FIRST VOICE
'But why drives on that ship so fast?
Without or wave or wind?'

SECOND VOICE
'The air is cut away before,
And closes from behind.
Fly, brother, fly! more high, more high!
Or we shall be belated:
For slow and slow that ship will go,
When the Mariner's trance is abated.

I woke, and we were sailing on
As in a gentle weather:
'T was night, calm night, the moon was high,
The dead men stood together.

All stood together on the deck,

For a charnel-dungeon fitter:
All fixed on me their stony eyes,
That in the Moon did glitter.

The pang, the curse, with which they died,
Had never passed away:
I could not draw my eyes from theirs,
Nor turn them up to pray.

And now this spell was snapt: once more
I viewed the ocean green,
And looked far forth, yet little saw
Of what had else been seen—

Like one, that on a lonesome road
Doth walk in fear and dread,
And having once turned round walks on,
And turns no more his head;
Because he knows, a frightful fiend
Doth close behind him tread.

But soon there breathed a wind on me,
Nor sound nor motion made:
Its path was not upon the sea,
In ripple or in shade.

It raised my hair, it fanned my cheek
Like a meadow-gale of spring—
It mingled strangely with my fears,
Yet it felt like a welcoming.

Swiftly, swiftly flew the ship,
Yet she sailed softly too:
Sweetly, sweetly blew the breeze—
On me alone it blew.

Oh! dream of joy! is this indeed
The light-house top I see?
Is this the hill? is this the kirk?
Is this mine own countree?

We drifted o'er the harbor-bar,

And I with sobs did pray—
O let me be awake, my God!
Or let me sleep alway.

The harbor-bay was clear as glass,
So smoothly it was strewn!
And on the bay the moonlight lay,
And the shadow of the Moon.

The rock shone bright, the kirk no less,
That stands above the rock:
The moonlight steeped in silentness
The steady weathercock.

And the bay was white with silent light
Till rising from the same,
Full many shapes, that shadows were,
In crimson colors came.

A little distance from the prow
Those crimson shadows were:
I turned my eyes upon the deck—
Oh, Christ! what saw I there!

Each corse lay flat, lifeless and flat,
And, by the holy rood!
A man all light, a seraph-man,
On every corse there stood.

This seraph-band, each waved his hand:
It was a heavenly sight!
They stood as signals to the land,
Each one a lovely light;
This seraph-band, each waved his hand,
No voice did they impart—
No voice; but oh! the silence sank
Like music on my heart.

But soon I heard the dash of oars,
I heard the Pilot's cheer;
My head was turned perforce away,
And I saw a boat appear.

The Pilot and the Pilot's boy,
I heard them coming fast:
Dear Lord in Heaven! it was a joy
The dead men could not blast.

I saw a third—I heard his voice:
It is the Hermit good!
He singeth loud his godly hymns
That he makes in the wood.
He'll shrieve my soul, he'll wash away
The Albatross's blood.

PART VII

This Hermit good lives in that wood
Which slopes down to the sea.
How loudly his sweet voice he rears!
He loves to talk with marineres
That come from a far countree.

He kneels at morn, and noon, and eve—
He hath a cushion plump:
It is the moss that wholly hides
The rotted old oak-stump.

The skiff-boat neared: I heard them talk,
'Why, this is strange, I trow!
Where are those lights, so many and fair,
That signal made but now?'

'Strange, by my faith!' the Hermit said—
'And they answered not our cheer!
The planks looked warped! and see those sails,
How thin they are and sere!
I never saw aught like to them,
Unless perchance it were

Brown skeletons of leaves that lag
My forest-brook along;
When the ivy-tod is heavy with snow,
And the owlet whoops to the wolf below,

That eats the she-wolf's young.'

'Dear Lord! it hath a fiendish look—
(The Pilot made reply)
I am a-feared'—'Push on, push on!'
Said the Hermit cheerily.

The boat came closer to the ship,
But I nor spake nor stirred;
The boat came close beneath the ship,
And straight a sound was heard.

Under the water it rumbled on,
Still louder and more dread:
It reached the ship, it split the bay;
The ship went down like lead.

Stunned by that loud and dreadful sound,
Which sky and ocean smote,
Like one that hath been seven days drowned
My body lay afloat;
But swift as dreams, myself I found
Within the Pilot's boat.

Upon the whirl, where sank the ship,
The boat spun round and round;
And all was still, save that the hill
Was telling of the sound.

I moved my lips—the Pilot shrieked
And fell down in a fit;
The holy Hermit raised his eyes,
And prayed where he did sit.
I took the oars: the Pilot's boy,
Who now doth crazy go,
Laughed loud and long, and all the while
His eyes went to and fro.
'Ha! ha!' quoth he, 'full plain I see,
The Devil knows how to row.'

And now, all in my own countree,
I stood on the firm land!

The Hermit stepped forth from the boat,
And scarcely he could stand.

'O shrieve me, shrieve me, holy man!'
The Hermit crossed his brow.
'Say quick,' quoth he, 'I bid thee say—
What manner of man art thou?'

Forthwith this frame of mine was wrenched
With a woful agony,
Which forced me to begin my tale;
And then it left me free.

Since then, at an uncertain hour,
That agony returns:
And till my ghastly tale is told,
This heart within me burns.

I pass, like night, from land to land;
I have strange power of speech;
That moment that his face I see,
I know the man that must hear me:
To him my tale I teach.

What loud uproar bursts from that door!
The wedding-guests are there:
But in the garden-bower the bride
And bride-maids singing are:
And hark the little vesper bell,
Which biddeth me to prayer!

O Wedding-Guest! this soul hath been
Alone on a wide, wide sea:
So lonely 't was, that God himself
Scarce seemed there to be.

O sweeter than the marriage-feast,
'T is sweeter far to me,
To walk together to the kirk
With a goodly company!—

To walk together to the kirk,

And all together pray,
While each to his great Father bends,
Old men, and babes, and loving friends
And youths and maidens gay!

Farewell, farewell! but this I tell
To thee, thou Wedding-Guest!
He prayeth well, who loveth well
Both man and bird and beast.

He prayeth best, who loveth best
All things both great and small;
For the dear God who loveth us,
He made and loveth all."

The Mariner, whose eye is bright,
Whose beard with age is hoar,
Is gone: and now the Wedding-Guest
Turned from the bridegroom's door.

He went like one that hath been stunned,
And is of sense forlorn:
A sadder and a wiser man,
He rose the morrow morn.

THE MARRIAGE OF HEAVEN AND HELL
(1790-1793)

WILLIAM BLAKE (1757-1827)

As the British Empire's COLONIALIST holdings expanded across the globe, so too did their contact with other cultures, which sometimes inspired a fetishism of what—to the European mindset—was the foreign or exotic. Orientalism in particular (an "othering" of Eastern cultures, particularly Arabic, Middle Eastern, Asian, and North African)—became a fancy of the ROMANTICS, who saw in their imagined East a corrective to the norms of their native West. That's a problematic assumption, of course, and the best we might say is that ROMANTIC poets like Percy Shelley (poet-husband of Mary Shelley) and Horace Smith (the Shelleys' poet-stockbroker) didn't mean any harm in their fetishism. Thus arose the twin poems "Ozymandias" and "On a Stupendous Leg of Granite." As was sometimes the past-time of idle poets at the time, the two—Percy and Horace—engaged in a sonnet contest, simultaneously drawing inspiration for their poetry from a much-anticipated archaeological exhibition due to hit the British Museum in 1818. Although the exhibit of Egyptian antiquities—including some enormous statuary remains depicting the pharaoh Ramesses II (known as Ozymandias among the Greeks)—was delayed, they nevertheless engaged in a stirring bout of literary EKPHRASIS, penning (and publishing) a pair of sonnets in which their narrators wax philosophical over the remains of a mighty statue in a desert. META!

Meanwhile (well, a few years earlier, really, but also in London), William Blake toiled over relief etchings, illuminating his own mystical poetry by acid-etching script and image onto copper plates, then hand-coloring the results. Like other ROMANTICS, Blake reacted strongly against the strict "logic" of the ENLIGHTENMENT; the mythological oppositions ("contraries") and seemingly paradoxical proverbs he offers in "The Marriage of Heaven and Hell" provide alternatives to orthodox beliefs, if not downright revolutionary notions designed to take down institutions. It takes a certain kind of genius to declare Good is passive, and Evil rebellious...and then note that Jesus was really a rebel. Even his most accessible poem—"The Tyger"—forces the reader to question traditional assumptions about God, creation...and symmetry. To many of his contemporaries, Blake seemed "mad" (and not solely from all the "acid-trips"). Yet a few generations later—a Beat Generation later, to be precise—Blake found recognition as a countercultural icon and inspirational poet.

THE ARGUMENT

Rintrah roars and shakes his
fires in the burden'd air,
Hungry clouds swag on the deep.

Once meek, and in a perilous path
The just man kept his course along
The Vale of Death.
Roses are planted where thorns grow,
And on the barren heath
Sing the honey bees.

Then the perilous path was planted,
And a river and a spring
On every cliff and tomb;
And on the bleached bones
Red clay brought forth:
Till the villain left the paths of ease
To walk in perilous paths, and drive
The just man into barren climes.

Now the sneaking serpent walks
In mild humility;
And the just man rages in the wilds
Where lions roam.

Rintrah roars and shakes his fires in
    the burdened air,
Hungry clouds swag on the deep.

  As a new heaven is begun, and it is
now thirty-three years since its advent,
the Eternal Hell revives. And lo!
Swedenborg is the angel sitting at
the tomb: his writings are the linen
clothes folded up. Now is the domin-

ion of Edom, and the return of Adam
into Paradise. — See Isaiah xxxiv. and
XXXV. chap.

Without contraries is no progression. Attraction and repulsion, reason
and energy, love and hate, are necessary to human existence.

From these contraries spring what the religious call Good and Evil.

Good is the passive that obeys reason; Evil is the active springing from
Energy.

Good is heaven. Evil is hell.

THE VOICE OF THE DEVIL

All Bibles or sacred codes have been the cause of the following errors
: —

1. That man has two real existing principles, viz., a Body and a Soul.

2. That Energy, called Evil, is alone from the Body ; and that Reason,
called Good, is alone from the Soul.

3. That God will torment man in Eternity for following his Energies.

But the following contraries to these are true : —

1 . Man has no Body distinct from his Soul. For that called Body is a
portion of Soul discerned by the five senses, the chief inlets of Soul in this
age.

2 . Energy is the only life, and is from the Body; and Reason is the bound
or outward circumference of Energy.

3. Energy is Eternal Delight.

Those who restrain desire, do so because theirs is weak enough to be
restrained; and the restrainer or
reason usurps its place and governs the unwilling.

And being restrained, it by degrees becomes passive, till it is only the
shadow of desire.

The history of this is written in Paradise Lost, and the Governor or
Reason is called Messiah.

And the original Archangel or possessor of the command of the heavenly
host is called the Devil, or Satan, and his children are called Sin and Death.

But in the book of Job, Milton's Messiah is called Satan.

For this history has been adopted by both parties.

It indeed appeared to Reason as if desire was cast out, but the Devil's account is, that the Messiah fell, and formed a heaven of what he stole from the abyss.

This is shown in the Gospel, where he prays to the Father to send the Comforter or desire that Reason may have ideas to build on, the Jehovah of the Bible being no other than he who dwells in flaming fire. Know that after Christ's death he became Jehovah.

But in Milton, the Father is Destiny, the Son a ratio of the five senses, and the Holy Ghost vacuum!

Note. — The reason Milton wrote in fetters when he wrote of Angels and God, and at liberty when of
Devils and Hell, is because he was a true poet, and of the Devil's party without knowing it.

A MEMORABLE FANCY

As I was walking among the fires of Hell, delighted with the enjoyments of Genius, which to Angels look like torment and insanity, I collected some of their proverbs, thinking that as the sayings used in a nation mark its character, so the proverbs of Hell show the nature of infernal wisdom better than any description of buildings or garments.

When I came home, on the abyss of the five senses, where a flat-sided steep frowns over the present world, I saw a mighty Devil folded in black clouds hovering on the sides of the rock; with corroding fires he wrote the following sentence now perceived by the minds of men, and read by them on earth : —

"How do you know but every bird
   that cuts the airy way
Is an immense world of delight,
   closed by your senses five?"

PROVERBS OF HELL

In seed-time learn, in harvest teach, in winter enjoy.
Drive your cart and your plough over the bones of the dead.
The road of excess leads to the palace of wisdom.
Prudence is a rich ugly old maid courted by Incapacity.
He who desires, but acts not, breeds pestilence.
The cut worm forgives the plough.

Dip him in the river who loves water.

A fool sees not the same tree that a wise man sees.

He whose face gives no light shall never become a star.

Eternity is in love with the productions of time.

The busy bee has no time for sorrow.

The hours of folly are measured by the clock, but of wisdom no clock can measure.

All wholesome food is caught without a net or a trap.

Bring out number, weight, and measure in a year of dearth.

No bird soars too high if he soars with his own wings.

A dead body revenges not injuries.

The most sublime act is to set another before you.

If the fool would persist in his folly he would become wise.

Folly is the cloak of knavery.

Shame is Pride's cloak.

Prisons are built with stones of law, brothels with bricks of religion.

The pride of the peacock is the glory of God.

The lust of the goat is the bounty of God.

The wrath of the lion is the wisdom of God.

The nakedness of woman is the work of God.

Excess of sorrow laughs, excess of joy weeps.

The roaring of lions, the howling of wolves, the raging of the stormy sea, and the destructive sword, are portions of Eternity too great for the eye of man.

The fox condemns the trap, not himself.

Joys impregnate, sorrows bring forth.

Let man wear the fell of the lion, woman the fleece of the sheep.

The bird a nest, the spider a web, man friendship.

The selfish smiling fool and the sullen frowning fool shall be both thought wise that they may be a rod.

What is now proved was once only imagined.

The rat, the mouse, the fox, the rabbit watch the roots; the lion, the tiger, the horse, the elephant watch the fruits.

The cistern contains, the fountain overflows.

One thought fills immensity.

Always be ready to speak your mind, and a base man will avoid you.

Everything possible to be believed is an image of truth.

The eagle never lost so much time as when he submitted to learn of the crow.

The fox provides for himself, but God provides for the lion.

Think in the morning, act in the noon, eat in the evening, sleep in the night.

He who has suffered you to impose on him knows you.

As the plough follows words, so God rewards prayers.

The tigers of wrath are wiser than the horses of instruction.

Expect poison from the standing water.

You never know what is enough unless you know what is more than enough.

Listen to the fool's reproach; it is a kingly title.

The eyes of fire, the nostrils of air, the mouth of water, the beard of earth.

The weak in courage is strong in cunning.

The apple tree never asks the beech how he shall grow, nor the lion the horse how he shall take his prey.

The thankful receiver bears a plentiful harvest.

If others had not been foolish we should have been so.

The soul of sweet delight can never be defiled.

When thou seest an eagle, thou seest a portion of Genius. Lift up thy head!

As the caterpillar chooses the fairest leaves to lay her eggs on, so the priest lays his curse on the fairest joys.

To create a little flower is the labour of ages.

Damn braces; bless relaxes.

The best wine is the oldest, the best water the newest.

Prayers plough not; praises reap not; joys laugh not; sorrows weep not.

The head Sublime, the heart Pathos, the genitals Beauty, the hands and feet Proportion.

As the air to a bird, or the sea to a fish, so is contempt to the contemptible.

The crow wished everything was black; the owl that everything was white.

Exuberance is Beauty.

If the lion was advised by the fox, he would be cunning.

Improvement makes straight roads, but the crooked roads without Improvement are roads of Genius.

Sooner murder an infant in its cradle than nurse unacted desires.

Where man is not, nature is barren.

Truth can never be told so as to be understood and not to be believed.

Enough! or Too much.

The ancient poets animated all sensible objects with Gods or Geniuses, calling them by the names and adorning them with properties of woods, rivers, mountains, lakes, cities, nations, and whatever their enlarged and numerous senses could perceive. And particularly they studied the Genius of each city and country, placing it under its mental deity. Till a system was formed, which some took advantage of and enslaved the vulgar by attempting to realize or abstract the mental deities from their objects. Thus began Priesthood.

Choosing forms of worship from poetic tales.   And at length they pronounced that the Gods had ordered
such things. Thus men forgot that all deities reside in the human breast.

A MEMORABLE FANCY

The Prophets Isaiah and Ezekiel dined with me, and I asked them how they dared so roundly to assert that God spoke to them, and whether they did not think at the time that they would be misunderstood, and so be the cause of imposition.

Isaiah answered: "I saw no God, nor heard any, in a finite organical perception: but my senses discovered the infinite in everything; and as I was then persuaded, and remained confirmed, that the voice of honest indignation is the voice of God, I cared not for consequences, but wrote."

Then I asked: "Does a firm persuasion that a thing is so, make it so?"

He replied: "All poets believe that it does, and in ages of imagination this firm persuasion removed mountains; but many are not capable of a firm persuasion of anything."

Then Ezekiel said: "The philosophy of the East taught the first principles of human perception; some nations held one principle for the origin, and some another. We of Israel taught that the Poetic Genius (as you now call it) was the first principle, and all the others merely derivative, which was the cause of
our despising the Priests and Philosophers of other countries, and prophesying that all Gods would at last be proved to originate in ours, and to be the tributaries of the Poetic Genius. It was this that our great poet King David desired so fervently, and invokes so pathetically, saying by this he conquers enemies and governs kingdoms; and we so loved our God that we cursed in His name all the deities of surrounding nations, and asserted that they had rebelled. From these opinions the vulgar came to think that all nations would at last be subject to the Jews."

"This," said he, "like all firm per- suasions, is come to pass, for all nations believe the Jews' code, and worship the Jews' God; and what greater subjection can be?"

I heard this with some wonder, and must confess my own conviction. After dinner I asked Isaiah to favour the world with his lost works; he said none of equal value was lost. Ezekiel said the same of his.

I also asked Isaiah what made him go naked and barefoot three years. He answered: "The same that made our friend Diogenes the Grecian."

I then asked Ezekiel why he ate dung, and lay so long on his right and left side. He answered: "The desire of raising other men into a perception of the infinite. This the North American tribes practise. And is he honest who resists his genius or conscience, only for the sake of present ease or gratification?"

The ancient tradition that the world will be consumed in fire at the end of six thousand years is true, as I have heard from Hell.

For the cherub with his flaming sword is hereby commanded to leave his guard at [the] tree of life, and
when he does, the whole creation will be consumed and appear infinite and holy, whereas it now appears finite and corrupt.

This will come to pass by an improvement of sensual enjoyment.

But first the notion that man has a body distinct from his soul is to be expunged; this I shall do by printing in the infernal method by corrosives, which in Hell are salutary and medicinal, melting apparent surfaces away, and displaying the infinite which was hid.

If the doors of perception were cleansed everything would appear to man as it is, infinite.

For man has closed himself up, till he sees all things through narrow chinks of his cavern.

A MEMORABLE FANCY

I was in a printing-house in Hell, and saw the method in which knowledge is transmitted from generation to generation.

In the first chamber was a dragon-man, clearing away the rubbish from a cave's mouth; within, a number of dragons were hollowing the cave.

In the second chamber was a viper folding round the rock and the cave, and others adorning it with gold, silver, and precious stones.

In the third chamber was an eagle with wings and feathers of air; he caused the inside of the cave to be infinite; around were numbers of eagle-like men, who built palaces in the immense cliffs.

In the fourth chamber were lions of flaming fire raging around and melting the metals into living fluids.

In the fifth chamber were unnamed forms, which cast the metals into the expanse.

There they were received by men who occupied the sixth chamber, and took the forms of books, and were arranged in libraries.

The Giants who formed this world into its sensual existence and now seem to live in it in chains are in

truth the causes of its life and the sources of all activity, but the chains are the cunning of weak and tame minds, which have power to resist energy, according to the proverb, "The weak in courage is strong in cunning."

Thus one portion of being is the Prolific, the other the Devouring. To the devourer it seems as if the producer was in his chains; but it is not so, he only takes portions of existence, and fancies that the whole.

But the Prolific would cease to be prolific unless the Devourer as a sea received the excess of his delights.

Some will say, "Is not God alone the Prolific?" I answer: "God only acts and is in existing beings or men."

These two classes of men are always upon earth, and they should be enemies: whoever tries to reconcile them seeks to destroy existence.

Religion is an endeavour to reconcile the two.

Note. — Jesus Christ did not wish to unite but to separate them, as in the parable of sheep and goats; and He says : "I came not to send peace, but a sword."

Messiah, or Satan, or Tempter, was formerly thought to be one of the antediluvians who are our Energies.

A MEMORABLE FANCY

An Angel came to me and said: "O pitiable foolish young man! O horrible, O dreadful state! Consider the

hot burning dungeon thou art preparing for thyself to all Eternity, to which thou art going in such career."

I said : "Perhaps you will be willing to show me my eternal lot, and we will contemplate together upon it, and see whether your lot or mine is most desirable."

So he took me through a stable, and through a church, and down into the church vault, at the end of which was a mill; through the mill we went, and came to a cave; down the winding cavern we groped our tedious way, till

a void boundless as a nether sky appeared beneath us, and we held by the roots of trees, and hung over this immensity; but I said: "If you please, we will commit ourselves to this void,
and see whether Providence is here also; if you will not, I will." But he answered : "Do not presume, young man; but as we here remain, beholdthy lot, which will soon appear when the darkness passes away."

So I remained with him sitting in the twisted root of an oak; he was suspended in a fungus, which hung
with the head downward into the deep.

By degrees we beheld the infinite abyss, fiery as the smoke of a burning city; beneath us at an immense distance was the sun, black but shining; round it were fiery tracks on which revolved vast spiders, crawling after their prey, which flew, or rather swum, in the infinite deep, in the most terrific shapes of animals sprung from corruption; and the air was full of them, and seemed composed of them. These are Devils, and are called powers of the air. I now asked my companion which was my eternal lot. He said: "Between the black and white spiders."

But now, from between the black and white spiders, a cloud and fire burst and rolled through the deep, blackening all beneath so that the nether deep grew black as a sea, and rolled with a terrible noise. Beneath us was nothing now to be seen but a black tempest, till looking East be- tween the clouds and the waves, we saw a cataract of blood mixed with fire, and not many stones' throw from us appeared and sunk again the scaly fold of a monstrous serpent. At last to the East, distant about three degrees, appeared a fiery crest above the waves; slowly it reared like a ridge of golden rocks, till we discovered two globes of crimson fire, from which the sea fled away in clouds of smoke; and now we saw it was the head of Leviathan. His forehead was divided into streaks of green and purple, like those on a tiger's forehead; soon we saw his mouth and red gills hang just above the raging foam, tinging the
black deeps with beams of blood, advancing toward us with all the fury of a spiritual existence.

My friend the Angel climbed up from his station into the mill. I remained alone, and then this appearance was no more; but I found myself sitting on a pleasant bank beside a river by moonlight, hearing a harper who sung to the harp; and his theme was: "The man who never alters his
opinion is like standing water, and breeds reptiles of the mind."

But I arose, and sought for the mill, and there I found my Angel, who, surprised, asked me how I escaped.

I answered: "All that we saw was owing to your metaphysics; for when you ran away, I found myself on a bank by moonlight, hearing a harper. But now we have seen my eternal lot, shall I show you yours?" He laughed at my proposal; but I by force suddenly caught him in my arms, and flew Westerly through the night, till we were elevated above the earth's shadow; then I flung myself with him directly into the body of the sun; here I clothed myself in white, and taking in my hand Swedenborg's volumes, sunk from the glorious clime, and passed all the planets till we came to Saturn. Here I stayed to rest, and

then leaped into the void between Saturn and the fixed stars.

"Here," said I, "is your lot; in this space, if space it may be called." Soon we saw the stable and the church, and I took him to the altar and opened the Bible, and lo! it was a deep pit, into which I descended, driving the Angel before me. Soon we saw seven houses of brick. One we entered. In it were a number of monkeys, baboons, and all of that species, chained by the middle, grinning and snatching at one another, but withheld by the shortness of their chains. However, I saw that they sometimes grew numerous, and then the weak were caught by the strong, and with a grinning aspect, first coupled with and then devoured by plucking off first one limb and then another till the body was left a helpless trunk; this, after grinning and kissing it with seeming fondness, they devoured too. And here and there I saw one savourily picking the flesh off his own tail. As the stench terribly annoyed us both, we went into the

mill; and I in my hand brought the skeleton of a body, which in the mill was Aristotle's Analytics.

So the Angel said; "Thy phantasy has imposed upon me, and thou oughtest to be ashamed."

I answered: "We impose on one another, and it is but lost time to converse with you whose works are only Analytics."

"I have always found that Angels have the vanity to speak of themselves as the only wise; this they do

with a confident insolence sprouting from systematic reasoning.

"Thus Swedenborg boasts that what he writes is new ; though it is only the contents or index of already published books.

"A man carried a monkey about for a show, and because he was a little wiser than the monkey, grew vain, and conceived himself as much wiser than seven men. It is so with Swedenborg; he shows the folly of churches, and exposes hypocrites, till he imagines that all are religious, and himself the single one on earth that ever broke a net.

"Now hear a plain fact: Sweden- borg has not written one new truth. Now hear another: he has written all the old falsehoods.

"And now hear the reason: he conversed with Angels who are all religious, and conversed not with Devils who all hate religion, for he was incapable through his conceited notions.

"Thus Swedenborg's writings are a recapitulation of all superficial opinions, and an analysis of the more sublime, but no further.

"Have now another plain fact: any man of mechanical talents may from the writings of Paracelsus or Jacob Behmen produce ten thousand volumes of equal value with Swedenborg's, and from those of Dante or Shakespeare an infinite number.

"But when he has done this, let him not say that he knows better than his master, for he only holds a candle in sunshine."

A MEMORABLE FANCY

Once I saw a Devil in a flame of fire, who arose before an Angel that sat on a cloud, and the Devil uttered these words: "The worship of God is, honouring His gifts in other men each according to his genius, and loving the greatest men best. Those who envy or calumniate great men hate God, for there is no other God."

The Angel hearing this became almost blue, but mastering himself he grew yellow, and at last white-pink and smiling, and then replied: "Thou idolater, is not God One? and is not He visible in Jesus Christ? and has not Jesus Christ given His sanction to the law of ten commandments? and are not all other men fools, sinners, and nothings?"

The Devil answered: "Bray a fool in a mortar with wheat, yet shall not his folly be beaten out of him. If
Jesus Christ is the greatest man, you ought to love Him in the greatest degree. Now hear how He has given His sanction to the law of ten commandments. Did He not mock at the Sabbath, and so mock the Sabbath's God? murder those who were murdered because of Him? turn away the law from the woman taken in adultery, steal the labour of others to support Him? bear false witness when He omitted making a defence before Pilate? covet when He prayed for His disciples, and when He bid them shake off the dust of their feet against such as refused to lodge them? I tell you, no virtue can exist without break- ing these ten commandments. Jesus was all virtue, and acted from impulse, not from rules."

When he had so spoken, I beheld the Angel, who stretched out his arms embracing the flame of fire, and he was consumed, and arose as Elijah.

Note. — This Angel, who is now become a Devil, is my particular friend;

we often read the Bible together in its infernal or diabolical sense, which the world shall have if they behave well.

I have also the Bible of Hell, which the world shall have whether they will or no.

One law for the lion and ox is Oppression.

A SONG OF LIBERTY

1. The Eternal Female groan'd; it was heard over all the earth:

2. Albion's coast is sick silent; the American meadows faint.

3. Shadows of prophecy shiver along by the lakes and the rivers, and mutter across the ocean. France,
rend down thy dungeon!

4. Golden Spain, burst the barriers of old Rome!

5. Cast thy keys, O Rome, into the deep — down falling, even to eternity down falling;

6. And weep!

7. In her trembling hands she took the new-born terror, howling.

8. On those infinite mountains of light now barr'd out by the Atlantic sea, the new-born fire stood before the starry king.

9. Flagg'd with grey-brow'd snows and thunderous visages, the jealous wings wav'd over the deep.

10. The speary hand burn'd aloft; unbuckled was the shield; forth went the hand of jealousy among the flaming hair, and hurl'd the new-born wonder through the starry night.

11. The fire, the fire is falling !

12. Look up! look up! O citizen of London, enlarge thy countenance! O Jew, leave counting gold; return to thy oil and wine! O African, black African! (Go, winged thought, widen his forehead.)

13. The fiery limbs, the flaming hair shot like the sinking sun into the Western sea.

14. Wak'd from his eternal sleep, the hoary element roaring fled away.

15. Down rush'd, beating his wings in vain, the jealous king, his grey-brow'd councillors, thunderous warriors, curl'd veterans, among helms and shields, and chariots, horses, elephants, banners, castles, slings, and rocks.

16. Falling, rushing, ruining; buried in the ruins, on Urthona's dens.

17. All night beneath the ruins; then their sullen flames, faded, emerge round the gloomy king.

18. With thunder and fire, leading his starry hosts through the waste wilderness, he promulgates his ten commandments, glancing his beamy

eyelids over the deep in dark dismay.

19. Where the Son of Fire in his Eastern cloud, while the Morning plumes her golden breast,

20. Spuming the clouds written with curses, stamps the stony law to dust, loosing the eternal horses from the dens of night, crying: "Empire is no more! and now the lion and wolf shall cease."

CHORUS

Let the Priests of the Raven of
Dawn, no longer in deadly black, with
hoarse note curse the Sons of Joy.
Nor his accepted brethren whom,
tyrant, he calls free, lay the bound or
build the roof. Nor pale religious
lechery call that virginity that wishes,
but acts not!

For everything that lives is holy.

THE TYGER (from SONGS OF EXPERIENCE) (1794)

WILLIAM BLAKE (1757-1827)

Tyger! Tyger! burning bright
In the forests of the night,
What immortal hand or eye
Could frame thy fearful symmetry?
In what distant deeps or skies
Burnt the fire of thine eyes?
On what wings dare he aspire?
What the hand dare sieze the fire?
And what shoulder, & what art.
Could twist the sinews of thy heart?
And when thy heart began to beat,
What dread hand? & what dread feet?
What the hammer? what the chain?
In what furnace was thy brain?
What the anvil? what dread grasp
Dare its deadly terrors clasp?
When the stars threw down their spears,
And watered heaven with their tears,
Did he smile his work to see?
Did he who made the Lamb make thee?
Tyger! Tyger! burning bright
In the forests of the night,
What immortal hand or eye
Dare frame thy fearful symmetry?

William Blake's Title Page for *Songs of Innocence and of Experience Shewing the Two Contrary States of the Human Soul (1794)*

ON A STUPENDOUS LEG OF GRANITE, DISCOVERED STANDING BY ITSELF IN THE DESERTS OF EGYPT, WITH THE INSCRIPTION BELOW (1818)

HORACE SMITH (1779-1849)

In Egypt's sandy silence, all alone,
   Stands a gigantic leg, which far off throws
   The only shadow that the desert knows.
"I am great Ozymandias," saith the stone,
   "The king of kings: this mighty city shows
"The wonders of my hand." The city's gone!
   Nought but the leg remaining to disclose
The site of that forgotten Babylon.

We wonder, and some hunter may express
Wonder like ours, when thro' the wilderness,
   Where London stood, holding the wolf in chace,
He meets some fragment huge, and stops to guess
   What powerful, but unrecorded, race,
   Once dwelt in that annihilated place.

OZYMANDIAS (1818)

PERCY BYSSHE SHELLEY (1792-1822)

I met a traveller from an antique land
Who said: 'Two vast and trunkless legs of stone
Stand in the desert. Near them, on the sand,
Half sunk, a shattered visage lies, whose frown,
And wrinkled lip, and sneer of cold command,
Tell that its sculptor well those passions read
Which yet survive, stamped on these lifeless things,
The hand that mocked them and the heart that fed.
And on the pedestal these words appear —
"My name is Ozymandias, king of kings:
Look on my works, ye Mighty, and despair!"
Nothing beside remains. Round the decay
Of that colossal wreck, boundless and bare
The lone and level sands stretch far away.'

THE MURDERS IN THE RUE MORGUE (1841)

EDGAR ALLAN POE (1809-1849)

Edgar Allan Poe—author of such chilling short works as "The Raven," "The Fall of the House of Usher," The Tell-tale Heart," and "The Cask of Amontillado"—has earned a reputation as a GOTHIC writer extraordinaire for "good" reason: he was a master of the macabre, a hellish harbinger of horror, and grinning ghoul of the ghastly grotesque! Ahem. Yet his mastery of the popular GOTHIC genre was but one aspect of his creative output; in his short-lived heyday, Poe was a well-known literary critic, a sometime humorist, and a bit of a gossip columnist. Perhaps surprisingly, he is also known as the "father" of Detective Fiction—a decidedly REALIST genre—by virtue of three short stories revolving around his innovative crime-solving hero, C. Auguste Dupin: "The Murders in the Rue Morgue" (a seemingly supernatural locked-room mystery); "The Mystery of Marie Roget" (a real-world cold-case solved via armchair deduction); and "The Purloined Letter" (a master-class in criminal profiling).

The "mystery" genre predated Poe, of course (Sophocles' Oedipus Rex is arguably the earliest Western mystery), and "true crime" collections, penny dreadfuls, and broadsides enjoyed some popularity in the United States and England before he penned his first Dupin story. Yet in these three short stories, Poe articulates—in a fairly overt lit-crit fashion—three main attributes (two character-types and a narrative focus) for DETECTIVE FICTION that would define the genre throughout the AGE OF REALISM:

1. *the <u>Intellectual Hero</u> (or RATIOCINATOR), who employs analysis—a combination of both logic and imagination—to solve "supernatural" mysteries*
2. *the <u>Mystified Narrator</u> (or intermediary), who provides a lens for the reader to gain insight into the RATIOCINATOR's intellect*
3. *the focus on <u>Process over Solution</u>: intellectual gamesmanship— the act of solving a weird mystery—is more "fun" than actually solving the mystery ("justice" need not be served)*

In addition to these three hallmarks of Detective Fiction, Poe employs MACGUFFINS ("empty" quest items), Red Herrings (false leads), foolish foils (the police), and both "whodunit?" and "howzitdone?" plotlines: all fairly established elements of the mystery genres predating the Dupin stories.

  Poe's RATIOCINATOR (a term he coined before the word—or the real-world job title—"detective" existed) employs what modern TV dramas would term "forensics" and "profiling": both logical and creative analysis. For Poe, Dupin's ability to sift through evidential minutia is just as important as his ability to imagine how the perpetrator "thinks." The hero's intellectually average companion (unnamed in the Dupin stories) is necessary to bridge the gap between the hero's almost supernatural prescience and the reader's own concurrent RATIOCINATION; in a perfect bit of Detective Fiction, the reader should be offered enough information to solve the mystery alongside the hero—to match wits with hero and enjoy the process of the intellectual "game."

  Spoiler alert: Dupin does not "play fair"!

What song the Syrens sang, or what name Achilles assumed when he hid himself among women, although puzzling questions, are not beyond all conjecture. —Sir Thomas Browne.

The mental features discoursed of as the analytical, are, in themselves, but little susceptible of analysis. We appreciate them only in their effects. We know of them, among other things, that they are always to their possessor, when inordinately possessed, a source of the liveliest enjoyment. As the strong man exults in his physical ability, delighting in such exercises as call his muscles into action, so glories the analyst in that moral activity which disentangles. He derives pleasure from even the most trivial occupations bringing his talent into play. He is fond of enigmas, of conundrums, of hieroglyphics; exhibiting in his solutions of each a degree of acumen which appears to the ordinary apprehension praeternatural. His results, brought about by the very soul and essence of method, have, in truth, the whole air of intuition.

  The faculty of re-solution is possibly much invigorated by mathematical study, and especially by that highest branch of it which, unjustly, and merely on account of its retrograde operations, has been called, as if par excellence, analysis. Yet to calculate is not in itself to analyse. A chess-player, for example, does the one without effort at the other. It follows that the game of chess, in its effects upon mental character, is greatly misunderstood. I am not now writing a treatise, but simply prefacing a somewhat peculiar narrative by observations very much at random; I will, therefore, take occasion to assert that the higher powers of the reflective intellect are more decidedly and more usefully tasked by the unostentatious game of draughts than by all the elaborate frivolity of chess. In this latter, where the pieces have different and bizarre motions, with various and variable values, what is only complex is mistaken (a not unusual error) for what is profound. The attention is here called powerfully into play. If it flag for an instant, an oversight is committed resulting in injury or defeat. The possible moves being not only manifold but involute, the chances of such oversights are multiplied; and in nine cases out of ten it is the more concentrative rather than the more acute player who conquers. In draughts, on the contrary, where the moves are unique and have but little variation, the probabilities of inadvertence are diminished, and the mere attention being left comparatively unemployed, what advantages are obtained by either party are obtained by superior acumen. To be less abstract—Let us suppose a game of draughts where the pieces are reduced to four kings, and where, of course, no oversight is to be expected. It is obvious that here the victory can be decided (the players being at all equal) only by some re-cherché movement, the result of some strong exertion of the intellect. De-prived of ordinary resources, the analyst throws himself into the spirit of his opponent, identifies himself therewith, and not unfrequently sees thus, at a glance, the sole methods (sometime indeed absurdly simple ones) by which he may seduce into error or hurry into miscalculation.

Whist has long been noted for its influence upon what is termed the calculating power; and men of the highest order of intellect have been known to take an apparently unaccountable delight in it, while eschewing chess as frivolous. Beyond doubt there is nothing of a similar nature so greatly tasking the faculty of analysis. The best chess-player in Christen-dom may be little more than the best player of chess; but proficiency in whist implies capacity for success in all those more important undertak-ings where mind struggles with mind. When I say proficiency, I mean that perfection in the game which includes a comprehension of all the sources whence legitimate advantage may be derived. These are not only manifold but multiform, and lie frequently among recesses of thought altogether inaccessible to the ordinary understanding. To observe attentively is to re-member distinctly; and, so far, the concentrative chess-player will do very well at whist; while the rules of Hoyle (themselves based upon the mere mechanism of the game) are sufficiently and generally comprehensible. Thus to have a retentive memory, and to proceed by "the book," are points commonly regarded as the sum total of good playing. But it is in matters beyond the limits of mere rule that the skill of the analyst is evinced. He makes, in silence, a host of observations and inferences. So, perhaps, do his companions; and the difference in the extent of the information ob-tained, lies not so much in the validity of the inference as in the quality of the observation. The necessary knowledge is that of what to observe.

Our player confines himself not at all; nor, because the game is the object, does he reject deductions from things external to the game. He examines the countenance of his partner, comparing it carefully with that of each of his opponents. He considers the mode of assorting the cards in each hand; often counting trump by trump, and honor by honor, through the glances bestowed by their holders upon each. He notes every variation of face as the play progresses, gathering a fund of thought from the differences in the expression of certainty, of surprise, of triumph, or of chagrin. From the manner of gathering up a trick he judges whether the person taking it can make another in the suit. He recognises what is played through feint, by the air with which it is thrown upon the table. A casual or inadvertent word; the accidental dropping or turning of a card, with the accompanying anxiety or carelessness in regard to its concealment; the counting of the tricks, with the order of their arrangement; embarrassment, hesitation, eagerness or trepidation—all afford, to his apparently intuitive perception, indications of the true state of affairs. The first two or three rounds having been played, he is in full possession of the contents of each hand, and thenceforward puts down his cards with as absolute a precision of purpose as if the rest of the party had turned outward the faces of their own.

The analytical power should not be confounded with ample ingenuity; for while the analyst is necessarily ingenious, the ingenious man is often remarkably incapable of analysis. The constructive or combining power, by which ingenuity is usually manifested, and to which the phrenologists (I believe erroneously) have assigned a separate organ, supposing it a primitive faculty, has been so frequently seen in those whose intellect bordered otherwise upon idiocy, as to have attracted general observation among writers on morals. Between ingenuity and the analytic ability there exists a difference far greater, indeed, than that between the fancy and the imagination, but of a character very strictly analogous. It will be found, in fact, that the ingenious are always fanciful, and the truly imaginative never otherwise than analytic.

The narrative which follows will appear to the reader somewhat in the light of a commentary upon the propositions just advanced.

Residing in Paris during the spring and part of the summer of 18—, I there became acquainted with a Monsieur C. Auguste Dupin. This young gentleman was of an excellent—indeed of an illustrious family, but, by a variety of untoward events, had been reduced to such poverty that the energy of his character succumbed beneath it, and he ceased to bestir himself in the world, or to care for the retrieval of his fortunes. By courtesy of his creditors, there still remained in his possession a small remnant of his patrimony; and, upon the income arising from this, he managed, by means of a rigorous economy, to procure the necessaries of life, without troubling himself about its superfluities. Books, indeed, were his sole luxuries, and in Paris these are easily obtained.

Our first meeting was at an obscure library in the Rue Montmartre, where the accident of our both being in search of the same very rare and very remarkable volume, brought us into closer communion. We saw each other again and again. I was deeply interested in the little family history which he detailed to me with all that candor which a Frenchman indulges whenever mere self is his theme. I was astonished, too, at the vast extent of his reading; and, above all, I felt my soul enkindled within me by the wild fervor, and the vivid freshness of his imagination. Seeking in Paris the objects I then sought, I felt that the society of such a man would be to me a treasure beyond price; and this feeling I frankly confided to him. It was at length arranged that we should live together during my stay in the city; and as my worldly circumstances were somewhat less embarrassed than his own, I was permitted to be at the expense of renting, and furnishing in a style which suited the rather fantastic gloom of our common temper, a time-eaten and grotesque mansion, long deserted through superstitions into which we did not inquire, and tottering to its fall in a retired and desolate portion of the Faubourg St. Germain.

Had the routine of our life at this place been known to the world, we should have been regarded as madmen—although, perhaps, as madmen of a harmless nature. Our seclusion was perfect. We admitted no visitors. Indeed the locality of our retirement had been carefully kept a secret from my own former associates; and it had been many years since Dupin had ceased to know or be known in Paris. We existed within ourselves alone.

It was a freak of fancy in my friend (for what else shall I call it?) to be enamored of the Night for her own sake; and into this bizarrerie, as into all his others, I quietly fell; giving myself up to his wild whims with a perfect abandon. The sable divinity would not herself dwell with us always; but we could counterfeit her presence. At the first dawn of the morning we closed all the messy shutters of our old building; lighting a couple of tapers which, strongly perfumed, threw out only the ghastliest and feeblest of rays. By the aid of these we then busied our souls in dreams—reading, writing, or conversing, until warned by the clock of the advent of the true Darkness. Then we sallied forth into the streets arm in arm, continuing the topics of the day, or roaming far and wide until a late hour, seeking, amid the wild lights and shadows of the populous city, that infinity of mental excitement which quiet observation can afford.

At such times I could not help remarking and admiring (although from his rich ideality I had been prepared to expect it) a peculiar analytic ability in Dupin. He seemed, too, to take an eager delight in its exercise—if not exactly in its display—and did not hesitate to confess the pleasure thus derived. He boasted to me, with a low chuckling laugh, that most men, in respect to himself, wore windows in their bosoms, and was wont to follow up such assertions by direct and very startling proofs of his intimate knowledge of my own. His manner at these moments was frigid and abstract; his eyes were vacant in expression; while his voice, usually a rich tenor, rose into a treble which would have sounded petulantly but for the deliberateness and entire distinctness of the enunciation. Observing him in these moods, I often dwelt meditatively upon the old philosophy of the Bi-Part Soul, and amused myself with the fancy of a double Dupin—the creative and the resolvent.

Let it not be supposed, from what I have just said, that I am detailing any mystery, or penning any romance. What I have described in the Frenchman, was merely the result of an excited, or perhaps of a diseased intelligence. But of the character of his remarks at the periods in question an example will best convey the idea.

We were strolling one night down a long dirty street in the vicinity of the Palais Royal. Being both, apparently, occupied with thought, neither of us had spoken a syllable for fifteen minutes at least. All at once Dupin broke forth with these words:

"He is a very little fellow, that's true, and would do better for the Théâtre des Variétés."

"There can be no doubt of that," I replied unwittingly, and not at first observing (so much had I been absorbed in reflection) the extraordinary manner in which the speaker had chimed in with my meditations. In an instant afterward I recollected myself, and my astonishment was profound.

"Dupin," said I, gravely, "this is beyond my comprehension. I do not hesitate to say that I am amazed, and can scarcely credit my senses. How was it possible you should know I was thinking of ——-?" Here I paused, to ascertain beyond a doubt whether he really knew of whom I thought.

—"of Chantilly," said he, "why do you pause? You were remarking to yourself that his diminutive figure unfitted him for tragedy."

This was precisely what had formed the subject of my reflections. Chantilly was a quondam cobbler of the Rue St. Denis, who, becoming stage-mad, had attempted the rôle of Xerxes, in Crébillon's tragedy so called, and been notoriously Pasquinaded for his pains.

"Tell me, for Heaven's sake," I exclaimed, "the method—if method there is—by which you have been enabled to fathom my soul in this matter." In fact I was even more startled than I would have been willing to express.

"It was the fruiterer," replied my friend, "who brought you to the conclusion that the mender of soles was not of sufficient height for Xerxes et id genus omne."

"The fruiterer!—you astonish me—I know no fruiterer whomsoever."

"The man who ran up against you as we entered the street—it may have been fifteen minutes ago."

I now remembered that, in fact, a fruiterer, carrying upon his head a large basket of apples, had nearly thrown me down, by accident, as we passed from the Rue C —— into the thoroughfare where we stood; but what this had to do with Chantilly I could not possibly understand.

There was not a particle of charlatanerie about Dupin. "I will explain," he said, "and that you may comprehend all clearly, we will first retrace the course of your meditations, from the moment in which I spoke to you until that of the rencontre with the fruiterer in question. The larger links of the chain run thus—Chantilly, Orion, Dr. Nichols, Epicurus, Stereotomy, the street stones, the fruiterer."

There are few persons who have not, at some period of their lives, amused themselves in retracing the steps by which particular conclusions of their own minds have been attained. The occupation is often full of interest and he who attempts it for the first time is astonished by the apparently illimitable distance and incoherence between the starting-point and the goal. What, then, must have been my amazement when I heard the Frenchman speak what he had just spoken, and when I could not help acknowledging that he had spoken the truth. He continued:

"We had been talking of horses, if I remember aright, just before leaving the Rue C ——. This was the last subject we discussed. As we crossed into this street, a fruiterer, with a large basket upon his head, brushing quickly past us, thrust you upon a pile of paving stones collected at a spot where the causeway is undergoing repair. You stepped upon one of the loose fragments, slipped, slightly strained your ankle, appeared vexed or sulky, muttered a few words, turned to look at the pile, and then proceeded in silence. I was not particularly attentive to what you did; but observation has become with me, of late, a species of necessity.

"You kept your eyes upon the ground—glancing, with a petulant expression, at the holes and ruts in the pavement, (so that I saw you were still thinking of the stones,) until we reached the little alley called Lamartine, which has been paved, by way of experiment, with the overlapping and riveted blocks. Here your countenance brightened up, and, perceiving your lips move, I could not doubt that you murmured the word 'stereotomy,' a term very affectedly applied to this species of pavement. I knew that you could not say to yourself 'stereotomy' without being brought to think of atomies, and thus of the theories of Epicurus; and since, when we discussed this subject not very long ago, I mentioned to you how singularly, yet with how little notice, the vague guesses of that noble Greek had met with confirmation in the late nebular cosmogony, I felt that you could not avoid casting your eyes upward to the great nebula in Orion, and I certainly expected that you would do so. You did look up; and I was now assured that I had correctly followed your steps. But in that bitter tirade upon Chantilly, which appeared in yesterday's 'Musée,' the satirist, making some disgraceful allusions to the cobbler's change of name upon assuming the buskin, quoted a Latin line about which we have often conversed. I mean the line

Perdidit antiquum litera sonum.

"I had told you that this was in reference to Orion, formerly written Urion; and, from certain pungencies connected with this explanation, I was aware that you could not have forgotten it. It was clear, therefore, that you would not fail to combine the two ideas of Orion and Chantilly. That you did combine them I saw by the character of the smile which passed over your lips. You thought of the poor cobbler's immolation. So far, you had been stooping in your gait; but now I saw you draw yourself up to your full height. I was then sure that you reflected upon the diminutive figure of Chantilly. At this point I interrupted your meditations to remark that as, in fact, he was a very little fellow—that Chantilly—he would do better at the Théâtre des Variétés."

Not long after this, we were looking over an evening edition of the "Gazette des Tribunaux," when the following paragraphs arrested our attention.

"EXTRAORDINARY MURDERS.—This morning, about three o'clock, the inhabitants of the Quartier St. Roch were aroused from sleep by a succession of terrific shrieks, issuing, apparently, from the fourth story of a house in the Rue Morgue, known to be in the sole occupancy of one Madame L'Espanaye, and her daughter Mademoiselle Camille L'Espanaye. After some delay, occasioned by a fruitless attempt to procure admission in the usual manner, the gateway was broken in with a crowbar, and eight or ten of the neighbors entered accompanied by two gendarmes. By this time the cries had ceased; but, as the party rushed up the first flight of stairs, two or more rough voices in angry contention were distinguished and seemed to proceed from the upper part of the house. As the second landing was reached, these sounds, also, had ceased and everything remained perfectly quiet. The party spread themselves and hurried from room to room. Upon arriving at a large back chamber in the fourth story, (the door of which, being found locked, with the key inside, was forced open,) a spectacle presented itself which struck every one present not less with horror than with astonishment.

"The apartment was in the wildest disorder—the furniture broken and thrown about in all directions. There was only one bedstead; and from this the bed had been removed, and thrown into the middle of the floor. On a chair lay a razor, besmeared with blood. On the hearth were two or three long and thick tresses of grey human hair, also dabbled in blood, and seeming to have been pulled out by the roots. Upon the floor were found four Napoleons, an ear-ring of topaz, three large silver spoons, three smaller of métal d'Alger, and two bags, containing nearly four thousand francs in gold. The drawers of a bureau, which stood in one corner were open, and had been, apparently, rifled, although many articles still remained in them. A small iron safe was discovered under the bed (not under the bedstead). It was open, with the key still in the door. It had no contents beyond a few old letters, and other papers of little consequence.

"Of Madame L'Espanaye no traces were here seen; but an unusual quantity of soot being observed in the fire-place, a search was made in the chimney, and (horrible to relate!) the corpse of the daughter, head downward, was dragged therefrom; it having been thus forced up the narrow aperture for a considerable distance. The body was quite warm. Upon examining it, many excoriations were perceived, no doubt occasioned by the violence with which it had been thrust up and disengaged. Upon the face were many severe scratches, and, upon the throat, dark bruises, and deep indentations of finger nails, as if the deceased had been throttled to death.

"After a thorough investigation of every portion of the house, without farther discovery, the party made its way into a small paved yard in the rear of the building, where lay the corpse of the old lady, with her throat so entirely cut that, upon an attempt to raise her, the head fell off. The body, as well as the head, was fearfully mutilated—the former so much so as scarcely to retain any semblance of humanity.

"To this horrible mystery there is not as yet, we believe, the slightest clew."

The next day's paper had these additional particulars.

"The Tragedy in the Rue Morgue. Many individuals have been examined in relation to this most extraordinary and frightful affair. [The word 'affaire' has not yet, in France, that levity of import which it conveys with us,] "but nothing whatever has transpired to throw light upon it. We give below all the material testimony elicited.

"Pauline Dubourg, laundress, deposes that she has known both the deceased for three years, having washed for them during that period. The old lady and her daughter seemed on good terms—very affectionate towards each other. They were excellent pay. Could not speak in regard to their mode or means of living. Believed that Madame L. told fortunes for a living. Was reputed to have money put by. Never met any persons in the house when she called for the clothes or took them home. Was sure that they had no servant in employ. There appeared to be no furniture in any part of the building except in the fourth story.

"Pierre Moreau, tobacconist, deposes that he has been in the habit of selling small quantities of tobacco and snuff to Madame L'Espanaye for nearly four years. Was born in the neighborhood, and has always resided there. The deceased and her daughter had occupied the house in which the corpses were found, for more than six years. It was formerly occupied by a jeweller, who under-let the upper rooms to various persons. The house was the property of Madame L. She became dissatisfied with the abuse of the premises by her tenant, and moved into them herself, refusing to let any portion. The old lady was childish. Witness had seen the daughter some five or six times during the six years. The two lived an exceedingly retired life—were reputed to have money. Had heard it said among the neighbors that Madame L. told fortunes—did not believe it. Had never seen any person enter the door except the old lady and her daughter, a porter once or twice, and a physician some eight or ten times.

"Many other persons, neighbors, gave evidence to the same effect. No one was spoken of as frequenting the house. It was not known whether there were any living connexions of Madame L. and her daughter. The shutters of the front windows were seldom opened. Those in the rear were always closed, with the exception of the large back room, fourth story. The house was a good house—not very old.

"Isidore Muset, gendarme, deposes that he was called to the house about three o'clock in the morning, and found some twenty or thirty persons at the gateway, endeavoring to gain admittance. Forced it open, at length, with a bayonet—not with a crowbar. Had but little difficulty in getting it open, on account of its being a double or folding gate, and bolted neither at bottom not top. The shrieks were continued until the gate was forced—and then suddenly ceased. They seemed to be screams of some person (or persons) in great agony—were loud and drawn out, not short and quick. Witness led the way up stairs. Upon reaching the first landing, heard two voices in loud and angry contention—the one a gruff voice, the other much shriller—a very strange voice. Could distinguish some words of the former, which was that of a Frenchman. Was positive that it was not a woman's voice. Could distinguish the words 'sacré' and 'diable.' The shrill voice was that of a foreigner. Could not be sure whether it was the voice of a man or of a woman. Could not make out what was said, but believed the language to be Spanish. The state of the room and of the bodies was described by this witness as we described them yesterday.

"Henri Duval, a neighbor, and by trade a silver-smith, deposes that he was one of the party who first entered the house. Corroborates the testimony of Muset in general. As soon as they forced an entrance, they reclosed the door, to keep out the crowd, which collected very fast, notwithstanding the lateness of the hour. The shrill voice, this witness thinks, was that of an Italian. Was certain it was not French. Could not be sure that it was a man's voice. It might have been a woman's. Was not acquainted with the Italian language. Could not distinguish the words, but was convinced by the intonation that the speaker was an Italian. Knew Madame L. and her daughter. Had conversed with both frequently. Was sure that the shrill voice was not that of either of the deceased.

"—Odenheimer, restaurateur. This witness volunteered his testimony. Not speaking French, was examined through an interpreter. Is a native of Amsterdam. Was passing the house at the time of the shrieks. They lasted for several minutes—probably ten. They were long and loud—very awful and distressing. Was one of those who entered the building. Corroborated the previous evidence in every respect but one. Was sure that the shrill voice was that of a man—of a Frenchman. Could not distinguish the words uttered. They were loud and quick—unequal—spoken apparently in fear as well as in anger. The voice was harsh—not so much shrill as harsh. Could not call it a shrill voice. The gruff voice said repeatedly 'sacré,' 'diable,' and once 'mon Dieu.'

"Jules Mignaud, banker, of the firm of Mignaud et Fils, Rue Deloraine. Is the elder Mignaud. Madame L'Espanaye had some property. Had opened an account with his banking house in the spring of the year—(eight years previously). Made frequent deposits in small sums. Had checked for nothing until the third day before her death, when she took out in person the sum of 4000 francs. This sum was paid in gold, and a clerk went home with the money.

"Adolphe Le Bon, clerk to Mignaud et Fils, deposes that on the day in question, about noon, he accompanied Madame L'Espanaye to her residence with the 4000 francs, put up in two bags. Upon the door being opened, Mademoiselle L. appeared and took from his hands one of the bags, while the old lady relieved him of the other. He then bowed and departed. Did not see any person in the street at the time. It is a bye-street—very lonely.

"William Bird, tailor deposes that he was one of the party who entered the house. Is an Englishman. Has lived in Paris two years. Was one of the first to ascend the stairs. Heard the voices in contention. The gruff voice was that of a Frenchman. Could make out several words, but cannot now remember all. Heard distinctly 'sacré' and 'mon Dieu.' There was a sound at the moment as if of several persons struggling—a scraping and scuffling sound. The shrill voice was very loud—louder than the gruff one. Is sure that it was not the voice of an Englishman. Appeared to be that of a German. Might have been a woman's voice. Does not understand German.

"Four of the above-named witnesses, being recalled, deposed that the door of the chamber in which was found the body of Mademoiselle L. was locked on the inside when the party reached it. Every thing was perfectly silent—no groans or noises of any kind. Upon forcing the door no person was seen. The windows, both of the back and front room, were down and firmly fastened from within. A door between the two rooms was closed, but not locked. The door leading from the front room into the passage was locked, with the key on the inside. A small room in the front of the house, on the fourth story, at the head of the passage was open, the door being ajar. This room was crowded with old beds, boxes, and so forth. These were carefully removed and searched. There was not an inch of any portion of the house which was not carefully searched. Sweeps were sent up and down the chimneys. The house was a four story one, with garrets (mansardes.) A trap-door on the roof was nailed down very securely—did not appear to have been opened for years. The time elapsing between the hearing of the voices in contention and the breaking open of the room door, was variously stated by the witnesses. Some made it as short as three minutes—some as long as five. The door was opened with difficulty.

"Alfonzo Garcio, undertaker, deposes that he resides in the Rue Morgue. Is a native of Spain. Was one of the party who entered the house. Did not proceed up stairs. Is nervous, and was apprehensive of the consequences of agitation. Heard the voices in contention. The gruff voice was that of a Frenchman. Could not distinguish what was said. The shrill voice was that of an Englishman—is sure of this. Does not understand the English language, but judges by the intonation.

"Alberto Montani, confectioner, deposes that he was among the first to ascend the stairs. Heard the voices in question. The gruff voice was that of a Frenchman. Distinguished several words. The speaker appeared to be ex-postulating. Could not make out the words of the shrill voice. Spoke quick and unevenly. Thinks it the voice of a Russian. Corroborates the general testimony. Is an Italian. Never conversed with a native of Russia.

"Several witnesses, recalled, here testified that the chimneys of all the rooms on the fourth story were too narrow to admit the passage of a human being. By 'sweeps' were meant cylindrical sweeping brushes, such as are employed by those who clean chimneys. These brushes were passed up and down every flue in the house. There is no back passage by which any one could have descended while the party proceeded up stairs. The body of Mademoiselle L'Espanaye was so firmly wedged in the chimney that it could not be got down until four or five of the party united their strength.

"Paul Dumas, physician, deposes that he was called to view the bodies about day-break. They were both then lying on the sacking of the bed-stead in the chamber where Mademoiselle L. was found. The corpse of the young lady was much bruised and excoriated. The fact that it had been thrust up the chimney would sufficiently account for these appearances. The throat was greatly chafed. There were several deep scratches just below the chin, together with a series of livid spots which were evidently the impression of fingers. The face was fearfully discolored, and the eye-balls protruded. The tongue had been partially bitten through. A large bruise was discovered upon the pit of the stomach, produced, apparently, by the pressure of a knee. In the opinion of M. Dumas, Mademoiselle L'Espanaye had been throttled to death by some person or persons unknown. The corpse of the mother was horribly mutilated. All the bones of the right leg and arm were more or less shattered. The left tibia much splintered, as well as all the ribs of the left side. Whole body dreadfully bruised and discolored. It was not possible to say how the injuries had been inflicted. A heavy club of wood, or a broad bar of iron—a chair—any large, heavy, and obtuse weapon would have produced such results, if wielded by the hands of a very powerful man. No woman could have inflicted the blows with any weapon. The head of the deceased, when seen by witness, was entirely separated from the body, and was also greatly shattered. The throat had evidently been cut with some very sharp instrument—probably with a razor.

"Alexandre Etienne, surgeon, was called with M. Dumas to view the bodies. Corroborated the testimony, and the opinions of M. Dumas.

"Nothing farther of importance was elicited, although several other persons were examined. A murder so mysterious, and so perplexing in all its particulars, was never before committed in Paris—if indeed a murder has been committed at all. The police are entirely at fault—an unusual occurrence in affairs of this nature. There is not, however, the shadow of a clew apparent."

The evening edition of the paper stated that the greatest excitement still continued in the Quartier St. Roch—that the premises in question had been carefully re-searched, and fresh examinations of witnesses instituted, but all to no purpose. A postscript, however, mentioned that Adolphe Le Bon had been arrested and imprisoned—although nothing appeared to criminate him, beyond the facts already detailed.

Dupin seemed singularly interested in the progress of this affair—at least so I judged from his manner, for he made no comments. It was only after the announcement that Le Bon had been imprisoned, that he asked me my opinion respecting the murders.

I could merely agree with all Paris in considering them an insoluble mystery. I saw no means by which it would be possible to trace the murderer.

"We must not judge of the means," said Dupin, "by this shell of an examination. The Parisian police, so much extolled for acumen, are cunning, but no more. There is no method in their proceedings, beyond the method of the moment. They make a vast parade of measures; but, not unfrequently, these are so ill adapted to the objects proposed, as to put us in mind of Monsieur Jourdain's calling for his robe-de-chambre—pour mieux entendre la musique. The results attained by them are not unfrequently surprising, but, for the most part, are brought about by simple diligence and activity. When these qualities are unavailing, their schemes fail. Vidocq, for example, was a good guesser and a persevering man. But, without educated thought, he erred continually by the very intensity of his investigations. He impaired his vision by holding the object too close. He might see, perhaps, one or two points with unusual clearness, but in so doing he, necessarily, lost sight of the matter as a whole. Thus there is such a thing as being too profound. Truth is not always in a well. In fact, as regards the more important knowledge, I do believe that she is invariably superficial. The depth lies in the valleys where we seek her, and not upon the mountain-tops where she is found. The modes and sources of this kind of error are well typified in the contemplation of the heavenly bodies. To look at a star by glances—to view it in a side-long way, by turning toward it the exterior portions of the retina (more susceptible of feeble impressions of light than the interior), is to behold the star distinctly—is to have the best appreciation of its lustre—a lustre which grows dim just in proportion as we turn our vision fully upon it. A greater number of rays actually fall upon the eye in the latter case, but, in the former, there is the more refined capacity for comprehension. By undue profundity we perplex and enfeeble thought; and it is possible to make even Venus herself vanish from the firmament by a scrutiny too sustained, too concentrated, or too direct.

"As for these murders, let us enter into some examinations for ourselves, before we make up an opinion respecting them. An inquiry will afford us amusement," [I thought this an odd term, so applied, but said nothing] "and, besides, Le Bon once rendered me a service for which I am not ungrateful. We will go and see the premises with our own eyes. I know G——, the Prefect of Police, and shall have no difficulty in obtaining the necessary permission."

The permission was obtained, and we proceeded at once to the Rue Morgue. This is one of those miserable thoroughfares which intervene between the Rue Richelieu and the Rue St. Roch. It was late in the afternoon when we reached it; as this quarter is at a great distance from that in which we resided. The house was readily found; for there were still many persons gazing up at the closed shutters, with an objectless curiosity, from the opposite side of the way. It was an ordinary Parisian house, with a gateway, on one side of which was a glazed watch-box, with a sliding panel in the window, indicating a loge de concierge. Before going in we walked up the street, turned down an alley, and then, again turning, passed in the rear of the building—Dupin, meanwhile examining the whole neighborhood, as well as the house, with a minuteness of attention for which I could see no possible object.

Retracing our steps, we came again to the front of the dwelling, rang, and, having shown our credentials, were admitted by the agents in charge. We went up stairs—into the chamber where the body of Mademoiselle L'Espanaye had been found, and where both the deceased still lay. The disorders of the room had, as usual, been suffered to exist. I saw nothing beyond what had been stated in the "Gazette des Tribunaux." Dupin scrutinized every thing—not excepting the bodies of the victims. We then went into the other rooms, and into the yard; a gendarme accompanying us throughout. The examination occupied us until dark, when we took our departure. On our way home my companion stepped in for a moment at the office of one of the daily papers.

I have said that the whims of my friend were manifold, and that Je les ménageais:—for this phrase there is no English equivalent. It was his humor, now, to decline all conversation on the subject of the murder, until about noon the next day. He then asked me, suddenly, if I had observed any thing peculiar at the scene of the atrocity.

There was something in his manner of emphasizing the word "peculiar," which caused me to shudder, without knowing why.

"No, nothing peculiar," I said; "nothing more, at least, than we both saw stated in the paper."

"The 'Gazette,'" he replied, "has not entered, I fear, into the unusual horror of the thing. But dismiss the idle opinions of this print. It appears to me that this mystery is considered insoluble, for the very reason which should cause it to be regarded as easy of solution—I mean for the outré character of its features. The police are confounded by the seeming absence of motive—not for the murder itself—but for the atrocity of the murder. They are puzzled, too, by the seeming impossibility of reconciling the voices heard in contention, with the facts that no one was discovered up stairs but the assassinated Mademoiselle L'Espanaye, and that there were no means of egress without the notice of the party ascending. The wild disorder of the room; the corpse thrust, with the head downward, up the chimney; the frightful mutilation of the body of the old lady; these considerations, with those just mentioned, and others which I need not mention, have sufficed to paralyze the powers, by putting completely at fault the boasted acumen, of the government agents. They have fallen into the gross but common error of confounding the unusual with the abstruse. But it is by these deviations from the plane of the ordinary, that reason feels its way, if at all, in its search for the true. In investigations such as we are now pursuing, it should not be so much asked 'what has occurred,' as 'what has occurred that has never occurred before.' In fact, the facility with which I shall arrive, or have arrived, at the solution of this mystery, is in the direct ratio of its apparent insolubility in the eyes of the police."

I stared at the speaker in mute astonishment.

"I am now awaiting," continued he, looking toward the door of our apartment—"I am now awaiting a person who, although perhaps not the perpetrator of these butcheries, must have been in some measure implicat- ed in their perpetration. Of the worst portion of the crimes committed, it is probable that he is innocent. I hope that I am right in this supposition; for upon it I build my expectation of reading the entire riddle. I look for the man here—in this room—every moment. It is true that he may not arrive; but the probability is that he will. Should he come, it will be necessary to detain him. Here are pistols; and we both know how to use them when occasion demands their use."

I took the pistols, scarcely knowing what I did, or believing what I heard, while Dupin went on, very much as if in a soliloquy. I have already spoken of his abstract manner at such times. His discourse was addressed to myself; but his voice, although by no means loud, had that intonation which is commonly employed in speaking to some one at a great distance. His eyes, vacant in expression, regarded only the wall.

"That the voices heard in contention," he said, "by the party upon the stairs, were not the voices of the women themselves, was fully proved by the evidence. This relieves us of all doubt upon the question whether the old lady could have first destroyed the daughter and afterward have com- mitted suicide. I speak of this point chiefly for the sake of method; for the strength of Madame L'Espanaye would have been utterly unequal to the task of thrusting her daughter's corpse up the chimney as it was found; and the nature of the wounds upon her own person entirely preclude the idea of self-destruction. Murder, then, has been committed by some third party; and the voices of this third party were those heard in contention. Let me now advert—not to the whole testimony respecting these voices—but to what was peculiar in that testimony. Did you observe any thing peculiar about it?"

I remarked that, while all the witnesses agreed in supposing the gruff voice to be that of a Frenchman, there was much disagreement in regard to the shrill, or, as one individual termed it, the harsh voice.

"That was the evidence itself," said Dupin, "but it was not the peculiar- ity of the evidence. You have observed nothing distinctive. Yet there was something to be observed. The witnesses, as you remark, agreed about the gruff voice; they were here unanimous. But in regard to the shrill voice, the peculiarity is—not that they disagreed—but that, while an Italian, an En-glishman, a Spaniard, a Hollander, and a Frenchman attempted to describe it, each one spoke of it as that of a foreigner. Each is sure that it was not the voice of one of his own countrymen. Each likens it—not to the voice of an individual of any nation with whose language he is conversant—but the converse. The Frenchman supposes it the voice of a Spaniard, and 'might have distinguished some words had he been acquainted with the Spanish.' The Dutchman maintains it to have been that of a Frenchman; but we find it stated that 'not understanding French this witness was ex-amined through an interpreter.' The Englishman thinks it the voice of a German, and 'does not understand German.' The Spaniard 'is sure' that it was that of an Englishman, but 'judges by the intonation' altogether, 'as he has no knowledge of the English.' The Italian believes it the voice of a Russian, but 'has never conversed with a native of Russia.' A second Frenchman differs, moreover, with the first, and is positive that the voice was that of an Italian; but, not being cognizant of that tongue, is, like the Spaniard, 'convinced by the intonation.' Now, how strangely unusual must that voice have really been, about which such testimony as this could have been elicited!—in whose tones, even, denizens of the five great divisions of Europe could recognise nothing familiar! You will say that it might have been the voice of an Asiatic—of an African. Neither Asiatics nor Africans abound in Paris; but, without denying the inference, I will now merely call your attention to three points. The voice is termed by one witness 'harsh rather than shrill.' It is represented by two others to have been 'quick and unequal.' No words—no sounds resembling words—were by any witness mentioned as distinguishable.

"I know not," continued Dupin, "what impression I may have made, so far, upon your own understanding; but I do not hesitate to say that le-gitimate deductions even from this portion of the testimony—the portion respecting the gruff and shrill voices—are in themselves sufficient to en-gender a suspicion which should give direction to all farther progress in the investigation of the mystery. I said 'legitimate deductions;' but my meaning is not thus fully expressed. I designed to imply that the deduc-tions are the sole proper ones, and that the suspicion arises inevitably from them as the single result. What the suspicion is, however, I will not say just yet. I merely wish you to bear in mind that, with myself, it was sufficiently forcible to give a definite form—a certain tendency—to my inquiries in the chamber.

"Let us now transport ourselves, in fancy, to this chamber. What shall we first seek here? The means of egress employed by the murderers. It is not too much to say that neither of us believe in praeternatural events. Madame and Mademoiselle L'Espanaye were not destroyed by spirits. The doers of the deed were material, and escaped materially. Then how? Fortunately, there is but one mode of reasoning upon the point, and that mode must lead us to a definite decision.—Let us examine, each by each, the possible means of egress. It is clear that the assassins were in the room where Mademoiselle L'Espanaye was found, or at least in the room adjoining, when the party ascended the stairs. It is then only from these two apartments that we have to seek issues. The police have laid bare the floors, the ceilings, and the masonry of the walls, in every direction. No secret issues could have escaped their vigilance. But, not trusting to their eyes, I examined with my own. There were, then, no secret issues. Both doors leading from the rooms into the passage were securely locked, with the keys inside. Let us turn to the chimneys. These, although of ordinary width for some eight or ten feet above the hearths, will not admit, throughout their extent, the body of a large cat. The impossibility of egress, by means already stated, being thus absolute, we are reduced to the windows. Through those of the front room no one could have escaped without notice from the crowd in the street. The murderers must have passed, then, through those of the back room. Now, brought to this conclusion in so unequivocal a manner as we are, it is not our part, as reasoners, to reject it on account of apparent impossibilities. It is only left for us to prove that these apparent 'impossibilities' are, in reality, not such.

"There are two windows in the chamber. One of them is unobstructed by furniture, and is wholly visible. The lower portion of the other is hidden from view by the head of the unwieldy bedstead which is thrust close up against it. The former was found securely fastened from within. It resisted the utmost force of those who endeavored to raise it. A large gimlet-hole had been pierced in its frame to the left, and a very stout nail was found fitted therein, nearly to the head. Upon examining the other window, a similar nail was seen similarly fitted in it; and a vigorous attempt to raise this sash, failed also. The police were now entirely satisfied that egress had not been in these directions. And, therefore, it was thought a matter of supererogation to withdraw the nails and open the windows.

"My own examination was somewhat more particular, and was so for the reason I have just given—because here it was, I knew, that all apparent impossibilities must be proved to be not such in reality.

"I proceeded to think thus—a posteriori. The murderers did escape from one of these windows. This being so, they could not have refastened the sashes from the inside, as they were found fastened;—the consideration which put a stop, through its obviousness, to the scrutiny of the police in this quarter. Yet the sashes were fastened. They must, then, have the power of fastening themselves. There was no escape from this conclusion. I stepped to the unobstructed casement, withdrew the nail with some difficulty and attempted to raise the sash. It resisted all my efforts, as I had anticipated. A concealed spring must, I now know, exist; and this corroboration of my idea convinced me that my premises at least, were correct, however mysterious still appeared the circumstances attending the nails. A careful search soon brought to light the hidden spring. I pressed it, and, satisfied with the discovery, forbore to upraise the sash.

"I now replaced the nail and regarded it attentively. A person passing out through this window might have reclosed it, and the spring would have caught—but the nail could not have been replaced. The conclusion was plain, and again narrowed in the field of my investigations. The assassins must have escaped through the other window. Supposing, then, the springs upon each sash to be the same, as was probable, there must be found a difference between the nails, or at least between the modes of their fixture. Getting upon the sacking of the bedstead, I looked over the head-board minutely at the second casement. Passing my hand down behind the board, I readily discovered and pressed the spring, which was, as I had supposed, identical in character with its neighbor. I now looked at the nail. It was as stout as the other, and apparently fitted in the same manner—driven in nearly up to the head.

"You will say that I was puzzled; but, if you think so, you must have misunderstood the nature of the inductions. To use a sporting phrase, I had not been once 'at fault.' The scent had never for an instant been lost. There was no flaw in any link of the chain. I had traced the secret to its ultimate result,—and that result was the nail. It had, I say, in every respect, the appearance of its fellow in the other window; but this fact was an absolute nullity (conclusive us it might seem to be) when compared with the consideration that here, at this point, terminated the clew. 'There must be something wrong,' I said, 'about the nail.' I touched it; and the head, with about a quarter of an inch of the shank, came off in my fingers. The rest of the shank was in the gimlet-hole where it had been broken off. The fracture was an old one (for its edges were incrusted with rust), and had apparently been accomplished by the blow of a hammer, which had partially imbedded, in the top of the bottom sash, the head portion of the nail. I now carefully replaced this head portion in the indentation whence I had taken it, and the resemblance to a perfect nail was complete—the fissure was invisible. Pressing the spring, I gently raised the sash for a few inches; the head went up with it, remaining firm in its bed. I closed the window, and the semblance of the whole nail was again perfect.

"The riddle, so far, was now unriddled. The assassin had escaped through the window which looked upon the bed. Dropping of its own accord upon his exit (or perhaps purposely closed), it had become fastened by the spring; and it was the retention of this spring which had been mistaken by the police for that of the nail,—farther inquiry being thus considered unnecessary.

"The next question is that of the mode of descent. Upon this point I had been satisfied in my walk with you around the building. About five feet and a half from the casement in question there runs a lightning-rod. From this rod it would have been impossible for any one to reach the window itself, to say nothing of entering it. I observed, however, that the shutters of the fourth story were of the peculiar kind called by Parisian carpenters ferrades—a kind rarely employed at the present day, but frequently seen upon very old mansions at Lyons and Bordeaux. They are in the form of an ordinary door, (a single, not a folding door) except that the lower half is latticed or worked in open trellis—thus affording an excellent hold for the hands. In the present instance these shutters are fully three feet and a half broad. When we saw them from the rear of the house, they were both about half open—that is to say, they stood off at right angles from the wall. It is probable that the police, as well as myself, examined the back of the tenement; but, if so, in looking at these ferrades in the line of their breadth (as they must have done), they did not perceive this great breadth itself, or, at all events, failed to take it into due consideration. In fact, having once satisfied themselves that no egress could have been made in this quarter, they would naturally bestow here a very cursory examination. It was clear to me, however, that the shutter belonging to the window at the head of the bed, would, if swung fully back to the wall, reach to within two feet of the lightning-rod. It was also evident that, by exertion of a very unusual degree of activity and courage, an entrance into the window, from the rod, might have been thus effected.—By reaching to the distance of two feet and a half (we now suppose the shutter open to its whole extent) a robber might have taken a firm grasp upon the trellis-work. Letting go, then, his hold upon the rod, placing his feet securely against the wall, and springing boldly from it, he might have swung the shutter so as to close it, and, if we imagine the window open at the time, might even have swung himself into the room.

"I wish you to bear especially in mind that I have spoken of a very unusual degree of activity as requisite to success in so hazardous and so difficult a feat. It is my design to show you, first, that the thing might possibly have been accomplished:—but, secondly and chiefly, I wish to impress upon your understanding the very extraordinary—the almost praeternatural character of that agility which could have accomplished it.

"You will say, no doubt, using the language of the law, that 'to make out my case,' I should rather undervalue, than insist upon a full estimation of the activity required in this matter. This may be the practice in law, but it is not the usage of reason. My ultimate object is only the truth. My immediate purpose is to lead you to place in juxtaposition, that very unusual activity of which I have just spoken with that very peculiar shrill (or harsh) and unequal voice, about whose nationality no two persons could be found to agree, and in whose utterance no syllabification could be detected."

At these words a vague and half-formed conception of the meaning of Dupin flitted over my mind. I seemed to be upon the verge of comprehension without power to comprehend—men, at times, find themselves upon the brink of remembrance without being able, in the end, to remember. My friend went on with his discourse.

"You will see," he said, "that I have shifted the question from the mode of egress to that of ingress. It was my design to convey the idea that both were effected in the same manner, at the same point. Let us now revert to the interior of the room. Let us survey the appearances here. The drawers of the bureau, it is said, had been rifled, although many articles of apparel still remained within them. The conclusion here is absurd. It is a mere guess—a very silly one—and no more. How are we to know that the articles found in the drawers were not all these drawers had originally contained? Madame L'Espanaye and her daughter lived an exceedingly retired life—saw no company—seldom went out—had little use for numerous changes of habiliment. Those found were at least of as good quality as any likely to be possessed by these ladies. If a thief had taken any, why did he not take the best—why did he not take all? In a word, why did he abandon four thousand francs in gold to encumber himself with a bundle of linen? The gold was abandoned. Nearly the whole sum mentioned by Monsieur Mignaud, the banker, was discovered, in bags, upon the floor. I wish you, therefore, to discard from your thoughts the blundering idea of motive, engendered in the brains of the police by that portion of the evidence which speaks of money delivered at the door of the house. Co-incidences ten times as remarkable as this (the delivery of the money, and murder committed within three days upon the party receiving it), happen to all of us every hour of our lives, without attracting even momentary notice. Coincidences, in general, are great stumbling-blocks in the way of that class of thinkers who have been educated to know nothing of the theory of probabilities—that theory to which the most glorious objects of human research are indebted for the most glorious of illustration. In the present instance, had the gold been gone, the fact of its delivery three days before would have formed something more than a coincidence. It would have been corroborative of this idea of motive. But, under the real circumstances of the case, if we are to suppose gold the motive of this outrage, we must also imagine the perpetrator so vacillating an idiot as to have abandoned his gold and his motive together.

"Keeping now steadily in mind the points to which I have drawn your attention—that peculiar voice, that unusual agility, and that startling absence of motive in a murder so singularly atrocious as this—let us glance at the butchery itself. Here is a woman strangled to death by manual strength, and thrust up a chimney, head downward. Ordinary assassins employ no such modes of murder as this. Least of all, do they thus dispose of the murdered. In the manner of thrusting the corpse up the chimney, you will admit that there was something excessively outré—something altogether irreconcilable with our common notions of human action, even when we suppose the actors the most depraved of men. Think, too, how great must have been that strength which could have thrust the body up such an aperture so forcibly that the united vigor of several persons was found barely sufficient to drag it down!

"Turn, now, to other indications of the employment of a vigor most marvellous. On the hearth were thick tresses—very thick tresses—of grey human hair. These had been torn out by the roots. You are aware of the great force necessary in tearing thus from the head even twenty or thirty hairs together. You saw the locks in question as well as myself. Their roots (a hideous sight!) were clotted with fragments of the flesh of the scalp—sure token of the prodigious power which had been exerted in uprooting perhaps half a million of hairs at a time. The throat of the old lady was not merely cut, but the head absolutely severed from the body: the instrument was a mere razor. I wish you also to look at the brutal ferocity of these deeds. Of the bruises upon the body of Madame L'Espanaye I do not speak. Monsieur Dumas, and his worthy coadjutor Monsieur Etienne, have pronounced that they were inflicted by some obtuse instrument; and so far these gentlemen are very correct. The obtuse instrument was clearly the stone pavement in the yard, upon which the victim had fallen from the window which looked in upon the bed. This idea, however simple it may now seem, escaped the police for the same reason that the breadth of the shutters escaped them—because, by the affair of the nails, their perceptions had been hermetically sealed against the possibility of the windows having ever been opened at all.

"If now, in addition to all these things, you have properly reflected upon the odd disorder of the chamber, we have gone so far as to combine the ideas of an agility astounding, a strength superhuman, a ferocity brutal, a butchery without motive, a grotesquerie in horror absolutely alien from humanity, and a voice foreign in tone to the ears of men of many nations, and devoid of all distinct or intelligible syllabification. What result, then, has ensued? What impression have I made upon your fancy?"

I felt a creeping of the flesh as Dupin asked me the question. "A madman," I said, "has done this deed—some raving maniac, escaped from a neighboring Maison de Santé."

"In some respects," he replied, "your idea is not irrelevant. But the voices of madmen, even in their wildest paroxysms, are never found to tally with that peculiar voice heard upon the stairs. Madmen are of some nation, and their language, however incoherent in its words, has always the coherence of syllabification. Besides, the hair of a madman is not such as I now hold in my hand. I disentangled this little tuft from the rigidly clutched fingers of Madame L'Espanaye. Tell me what you can make of it."

"Dupin!" I said, completely unnerved; "this hair is most unusual—this is no human hair."

"I have not asserted that it is," said he; "but, before we decide this point, I wish you to glance at the little sketch I have here traced upon this paper. It is a fac-simile drawing of what has been described in one portion of the testimony as 'dark bruises, and deep indentations of finger nails,' upon the throat of Mademoiselle L'Espanaye, and in another, (by Messrs. Dumas and Etienne,) as a 'series of livid spots, evidently the impression of fingers.'

"You will perceive," continued my friend, spreading out the paper upon the table before us, "that this drawing gives the idea of a firm and fixed hold. There is no slipping apparent. Each finger has retained—possibly until the death of the victim—the fearful grasp by which it originally imbedded itself. Attempt, now, to place all your fingers, at the same time, in the respective impressions as you see them."

I made the attempt in vain.

"We are possibly not giving this matter a fair trial," he said. "The paper is spread out upon a plane surface; but the human throat is cylindrical. Here is a billet of wood, the circumference of which is about that of the throat. Wrap the drawing around it, and try the experiment again."

I did so; but the difficulty was even more obvious than before. "This," I said, "is the mark of no human hand."

"Read now," replied Dupin, "this passage from Cuvier."

It was a minute anatomical and generally descriptive account of the large fulvous Ourang-Outang of the East Indian Islands. The gigantic stature, the prodigious strength and activity, the wild ferocity, and the imitative propensities of these mammalia are sufficiently well known to all. I understood the full horrors of the murder at once.

"The description of the digits," said I, as I made an end of reading, "is in exact accordance with this drawing. I see that no animal but an Ourang-Outang, of the species here mentioned, could have impressed the indentations as you have traced them. This tuft of tawny hair, too, is identical in character with that of the beast of Cuvier. But I cannot possibly comprehend the particulars of this frightful mystery. Besides, there were two voices heard in contention, and one of them was unquestionably the voice of a Frenchman."

"True; and you will remember an expression attributed almost unanimously, by the evidence, to this voice,—the expression, 'mon Dieu!' This, under the circumstances, has been justly characterized by one of the witnesses (Montani, the confectioner,) as an expression of remonstrance or expostulation. Upon these two words, therefore, I have mainly built my hopes of a full solution of the riddle. A Frenchman was cognizant of the murder. It is possible—indeed it is far more than probable—that he was innocent of all participation in the bloody transactions which took place. The Ourang-Outang may have escaped from him. He may have traced it to the chamber; but, under the agitating circumstances which ensued, he could never have re-captured it. It is still at large. I will not pursue these guesses—for I have no right to call them more—since the shades of reflection upon which they are based are scarcely of sufficient depth to be appreciable by my own intellect, and since I could not pretend to make them intelligible to the understanding of another. We will call them guesses then, and speak of them as such. If the Frenchman in question is indeed, as I suppose, innocent of this atrocity, this advertisement which I left last night, upon our return home, at the office of 'Le Monde,' (a paper devoted to the shipping interest, and much sought by sailors,) will bring him to our residence."

He handed me a paper, and I read thus:

CAUGHT—In the Bois de Boulogne, early in the morning of the— inst., (the morning of the murder,) a very large, tawny Ourang-Outang of the Bornese species. The owner, (who is ascertained to be a sailor, belonging to a Maltese vessel,) may have the animal again, upon identifying it satisfactorily, and paying a few charges arising from its capture and keeping. Call at No. ——, Rue ——, Faubourg St. Germain—au troisième.

"How was it possible," I asked, "that you should know the man to be a sailor, and belonging to a Maltese vessel?"

"I do not know it," said Dupin. "I am not sure of it. Here, however, is a small piece of ribbon, which from its form, and from its greasy appearance, has evidently been used in tying the hair in one of those long queues of which sailors are so fond. Moreover, this knot is one which few besides sailors can tie, and is peculiar to the Maltese. I picked the ribbon up at the foot of the lightning-rod. It could not have belonged to either of the deceased. Now if, after all, I am wrong in my induction from this ribbon, that the Frenchman was a sailor belonging to a Maltese vessel, still I can have done no harm in saying what I did in the advertisement. If I am in error, he will merely suppose that I have been misled by some circumstance into which he will not take the trouble to inquire. But if I am right, a great point is gained. Cognizant although innocent of the murder, the Frenchman will naturally hesitate about replying to the advertisement—about demanding the Ourang-Outang. He will reason thus:—'I am innocent; I am poor; my Ourang-Outang is of great value—to one in my circumstances a fortune of itself—why should I lose it through idle apprehensions of danger? Here it is, within my grasp. It was found in the Bois de Boulogne—at a vast distance from the scene of that butchery. How can it ever be suspected that a brute beast should have done the deed? The police are at fault—they have failed to procure the slightest clew. Should they even trace the animal, it would be impossible to prove me cognizant of the murder, or to implicate me in guilt on account of that cognizance. Above all, I am known. The advertiser designates me as the possessor of the beast. I am not sure to what limit his knowledge may extend. Should I avoid claiming a property of so great value, which it is known that I possess, I will render the animal at least, liable to suspicion. It is not my policy to attract attention either to myself or to the beast. I will answer the advertisement, get the Ourang-Outang, and keep it close until this matter has blown over.'"

At this moment we heard a step upon the stairs.

"Be ready," said Dupin, "with your pistols, but neither use them nor show them until at a signal from myself."

The front door of the house had been left open, and the visitor had entered, without ringing, and advanced several steps upon the staircase. Now, however, he seemed to hesitate. Presently we heard him descending. Dupin was moving quickly to the door, when we again heard him coming up. He did not turn back a second time, but stepped up with decision, and rapped at the door of our chamber.

"Come in," said Dupin, in a cheerful and hearty tone.

A man entered. He was a sailor, evidently,—a tall, stout, and muscular-looking person, with a certain dare-devil expression of countenance, not altogether unprepossessing. His face, greatly sunburnt, was more than half hidden by whisker and mustachio. He had with him a huge oaken cudgel, but appeared to be otherwise unarmed. He bowed awkwardly, and bade us "good evening," in French accents, which, although somewhat Neufchatelish, were still sufficiently indicative of a Parisian origin.

"Sit down, my friend," said Dupin. "I suppose you have called about the Ourang-Outang. Upon my word, I almost envy you the possession of him; a remarkably fine, and no doubt a very valuable animal. How old do you suppose him to be?"

The sailor drew a long breath, with the air of a man relieved of some intolerable burden, and then replied, in an assured tone:

"I have no way of telling—but he can't be more than four or five years old. Have you got him here?"

"Oh no, we had no conveniences for keeping him here. He is at a livery stable in the Rue Dubourg, just by. You can get him in the morning. Of course you are prepared to identify the property?"

"To be sure I am, sir."

"I shall be sorry to part with him," said Dupin.

"I don't mean that you should be at all this trouble for nothing, sir," said the man. "Couldn't expect it. Am very willing to pay a reward for the finding of the animal—that is to say, any thing in reason."

"Well," replied my friend, "that is all very fair, to be sure. Let me think!—what should I have? Oh! I will tell you. My reward shall be this. You shall give me all the information in your power about these murders in the Rue Morgue."

Dupin said the last words in a very low tone, and very quietly. Just as quietly, too, he walked toward the door, locked it and put the key in his pocket. He then drew a pistol from his bosom and placed it, without the least flurry, upon the table.

The sailor's face flushed up as if he were struggling with suffocation. He started to his feet and grasped his cudgel, but the next moment he fell back into his seat, trembling violently, and with the countenance of death itself. He spoke not a word. I pitied him from the bottom of my heart.

"My friend," said Dupin, in a kind tone, "you are alarming yourself unnecessarily—you are indeed. We mean you no harm whatever. I pledge you the honor of a gentleman, and of a Frenchman, that we intend you no injury. I perfectly well know that you are innocent of the atrocities in the Rue Morgue. It will not do, however, to deny that you are in some measure implicated in them. From what I have already said, you must know that I have had means of information about this matter—means of which you could never have dreamed. Now the thing stands thus. You have done nothing which you could have avoided—nothing, certainly, which renders you culpable. You were not even guilty of robbery, when you might have robbed with impunity. You have nothing to conceal. You have no reason for concealment. On the other hand, you are bound by every principle of honor to confess all you know. An innocent man is now imprisoned, charged with that crime of which you can point out the perpetrator."

The sailor had recovered his presence of mind, in a great measure, while Dupin uttered these words; but his original boldness of bearing was all gone.

"So help me God," said he, after a brief pause, "I will tell you all I know about this affair;—but I do not expect you to believe one half I say—I would be a fool indeed if I did. Still, I am innocent, and I will make a clean breast if I die for it."

What he stated was, in substance, this. He had lately made a voyage to the Indian Archipelago. A party, of which he formed one, landed at Borneo, and passed into the interior on an excursion of pleasure. Himself and a companion had captured the Ourang-Outang. This companion dying, the animal fell into his own exclusive possession. After great trouble, occasioned by the intractable ferocity of his captive during the home voyage, he at length succeeded in lodging it safely at his own residence in Paris, where, not to attract toward himself the unpleasant curiosity of his neighbors, he kept it carefully secluded, until such time as it should recover from a wound in the foot, received from a splinter on board ship. His ultimate design was to sell it.

Returning home from some sailors' frolic the night, or rather in the morning of the murder, he found the beast occupying his own bed-room, into which it had broken from a closet adjoining, where it had been, as was thought, securely confined. Razor in hand, and fully lathered, it was sitting before a looking-glass, attempting the operation of shaving, in which it had no doubt previously watched its master through the key-hole of the closet. Terrified at the sight of so dangerous a weapon in the possession of an animal so ferocious, and so well able to use it, the man, for some moments, was at a loss what to do. He had been accustomed, however, to quiet the creature, even in its fiercest moods, by the use of a whip, and to this he now resorted. Upon sight of it, the Ourang-Outang sprang at once through the door of the chamber, down the stairs, and thence, through a window, unfortunately open, into the street.

The Frenchman followed in despair; the ape, razor still in hand, occasionally stopping to look back and gesticulate at its pursuer, until the latter had nearly come up with it. It then again made off. In this manner the chase continued for a long time. The streets were profoundly quiet, as it was nearly three o'clock in the morning. In passing down an alley in the rear of the Rue Morgue, the fugitive's attention was arrested by a light gleaming from the open window of Madame L'Espanaye's chamber, in the fourth story of her house. Rushing to the building, it perceived the lightning rod, clambered up with inconceivable agility, grasped the shutter, which was thrown fully back against the wall, and, by its means, swung itself directly upon the headboard of the bed. The whole feat did not occupy a minute. The shutter was kicked open again by the Ourang-Outang as it entered the room.

The sailor, in the meantime, was both rejoiced and perplexed. He had strong hopes of now recapturing the brute, as it could scarcely escape from the trap into which it had ventured, except by the rod, where it might be intercepted as it came down. On the other hand, there was much cause for anxiety as to what it might do in the house. This latter reflection urged the man still to follow the fugitive. A lightning rod is ascended without difficulty, especially by a sailor; but, when he had arrived as high as the window, which lay far to his left, his career was stopped; the most that he could accomplish was to reach over so as to obtain a glimpse of the interior of the room. At this glimpse he nearly fell from his hold through excess of horror. Now it was that those hideous shrieks arose upon the night, which had startled from slumber the inmates of the Rue Morgue. Madame L'Espanaye and her daughter, habited in their night clothes, had apparently been occupied in arranging some papers in the iron chest already mentioned, which had been wheeled into the middle of the room. It was open, and its contents lay beside it on the floor. The victims must have been sitting with their backs toward the window; and, from the time elapsing between the ingress of the beast and the screams, it seems probable that it was not immediately perceived. The flapping-to of the shutter would naturally have been attributed to the wind.

As the sailor looked in, the gigantic animal had seized Madame L'Espanaye by the hair, (which was loose, as she had been combing it,) and was flourishing the razor about her face, in imitation of the motions of a barber. The daughter lay prostrate and motionless; she had swooned. The screams and struggles of the old lady (during which the hair was torn from her head) had the effect of changing the probably pacific purposes of the Ourang-Outang into those of wrath. With one determined sweep of its muscular arm it nearly severed her head from her body. The sight of blood inflamed its anger into phrenzy. Gnashing its teeth, and flashing fire from its eyes, it flew upon the body of the girl, and imbedded its fearful talons in her throat, retaining its grasp until she expired. Its wandering and wild glances fell at this moment upon the head of the bed, over which the face of its master, rigid with horror, was just discernible. The fury of the beast, who no doubt bore still in mind the dreaded whip, was instantly converted into fear. Conscious of having deserved punishment, it seemed desirous of concealing its bloody deeds, and skipped about the chamber in an agony of nervous agitation; throwing down and breaking the furniture as it moved, and dragging the bed from the bedstead. In conclusion, it seized first the corpse of the daughter, and thrust it up the chimney, as it was found; then that of the old lady, which it immediately hurled through the window head-long.

As the ape approached the casement with its mutilated burden, the sailor shrank aghast to the rod, and, rather gliding than clambering down it, hurried at once home—dreading the consequences of the butchery, and gladly abandoning, in his terror, all solicitude about the fate of the Ourang-Outang. The words heard by the party upon the staircase were the Frenchman's exclamations of horror and affright, commingled with the fiendish jabberings of the brute.

I have scarcely anything to add. The Ourang-Outang must have escaped from the chamber, by the rod, just before the break of the door. It must have closed the window as it passed through it. It was subsequently caught by the owner himself, who obtained for it a very large sum at the Jardin des Plantes. Le Don was instantly released, upon our narration of the circumstances (with some comments from Dupin) at the bureau of the Prefect of Police. This functionary, however well disposed to my friend, could not altogether conceal his chagrin at the turn which affairs had taken, and was fain to indulge in a sarcasm or two, about the propriety of every person minding his own business.

"Let him talk," said Dupin, who had not thought it necessary to reply. "Let him discourse; it will ease his conscience, I am satisfied with having defeated him in his own castle. Nevertheless, that he failed in the solution of this mystery, is by no means that matter for wonder which he supposes it; for, in truth, our friend the Prefect is somewhat too cunning to be profound. In his wisdom is no stamen. It is all head and no body, like the pictures of the Goddess Laverna,—or, at best, all head and shoulders, like a codfish. But he is a good creature after all. I like him especially for one master stroke of cant, by which he has attained his reputation for ingenuity. I mean the way he has *'de nier ce qui est, et d'expliquer ce qui n'est pas.'*"

THE PURLOINED LETTER (1844)

EDGAR ALLAN POE (1809-1849)

Nil sapientiae odiosius acumine nimio. - Seneca.

At Paris, just after dark one gusty evening in the autumn of 18-, I was enjoying the twofold luxury of meditation and a meerschaum, in company with my friend C. Auguste Dupin, in his little back library, or book-closet, au troisiême, No. 33, Rue Dunôt, Faubourg St. Germain. For one hour at least we had maintained a profound silence; while each, to any casual observer, might have seemed intently and exclusively occupied with the curling eddies of smoke that oppressed the atmosphere of the chamber. For myself, however, I was mentally discussing certain topics which had formed matter for conversation between us at an earlier period of the evening; I mean the affair of the Rue Morgue, and the mystery attending the murder of Marie Rogêt. I looked upon it, therefore, as something of a coincidence, when the door of our apartment was thrown open and admitted our old acquaintance, Monsieur G—, the Prefect of the Parisian police.

We gave him a hearty welcome; for there was nearly half as much of the entertaining as of the contemptible about the man, and we had not seen him for several years. We had been sitting in the dark, and Dupin now arose for the purpose of lighting a lamp, but sat down again, without doing so, upon G.'s saying that he had called to consult us, or rather to ask the opinion of my friend, about some official business which had occasioned a great deal of trouble.

"If it is any point requiring reflection," observed Dupin, as he forebore to enkindle the wick, "we shall examine it to better purpose in the dark."

"That is another of your odd notions," said the Prefect, who had a fashion of calling every thing "odd" that was beyond his comprehension, and thus lived amid an absolute legion of "oddities."

"Very true," said Dupin, as he supplied his visiter with a pipe, and rolled towards him a comfortable chair.

"And what is the difficulty now?" I asked. "Nothing more in the assassination way, I hope?"

"Oh no; nothing of that nature. The fact is, the business is very simple indeed, and I make no doubt that we can manage it sufficiently well ourselves; but then I thought Dupin would like to hear the details of it, because it is so excessively odd."

"Simple and odd," said Dupin.

"Why, yes; and not exactly that, either. The fact is, we have all been a good deal puzzled because the affair is so simple, and yet baffles us altogether."

"Perhaps it is the very simplicity of the thing which puts you at fault," said my friend.

"What nonsense you do talk!" replied the Prefect, laughing heartily.

"Perhaps the mystery is a little too plain," said Dupin.

"Oh, good heavens! Who ever heard of such an idea?"

"A little too self-evident."

"Ha! ha! ha—ha! ha! ha!—ho! ho! ho!" roared our visiter, profoundly amused, "oh, Dupin, you will be the death of me yet!"

"And what, after all, is the matter on hand?" I asked.

"Why, I will tell you," replied the Prefect, as he gave a long, steady and contemplative puff, and settled himself in his chair. "I will tell you in a few words; but, before I begin, let me caution you that this is an affair demanding the greatest secrecy, and that I should most probably lose the position I now hold, were it known that I confided it to any one."

"Proceed," said I.

"Or not," said Dupin.

"Well, then; I have received personal information, from a very high quarter, that a certain document of the last importance, has been purloined from the royal apartments. The individual who purloined it is known; this beyond a doubt; he was seen to take it. It is known, also, that it still remains in his possession."

"How is this known?" asked Dupin.

"It is clearly inferred," replied the Prefect, "from the nature of the document, and from the non-appearance of certain results which would at once arise from its passing out of the robber's possession; that is to say, from his employing it as he must design in the end to employ it."

"Be a little more explicit," I said.

"Well, I may venture so far as to say that the paper gives its holder a certain power in a certain quarter where such power is immensely valuable." The Prefect was fond of the cant of diplomacy.

"Still I do not quite understand," said Dupin.

"No? Well; the disclosure of the document to a third person, who shall be nameless, would bring in question the honor of a personage of most exalted station; and this fact gives the holder of the document an ascendancy over the illustrious personage whose honor and peace are so jeopardized."

"But this ascendancy," I interposed, "would depend upon the robber's knowledge of the loser's knowledge of the robber. Who would dare—"

"The thief," said G., "is the Minister D—, who dares all things, those unbecoming as well as those becoming a man. The method of the theft was not less ingenious than bold. The document in question—a letter, to be frank—had been received by the personage robbed while alone in the royal boudoir. During its perusal she was suddenly interrupted by the entrance of the other exalted personage from whom especially it was her wish to conceal it. After a hurried and vain endeavor to thrust it in a drawer, she was forced to place it, open as it was, upon a table. The address, however, was uppermost, and, the contents thus unexposed, the letter escaped notice. At this juncture enters the Minister D—. His lynx eye immediately perceives the paper, recognises the handwriting of the address, observes the confusion of the personage addressed, and fathoms her secret. After some business transactions, hurried through in his ordinary manner, he produces a letter somewhat similar to the one in question, opens it, pretends to read it, and then places it in close juxtaposition to the other. Again he converses, for some fifteen minutes, upon the public affairs. At length, in taking leave, he takes also from the table the letter to which he had no claim. Its rightful owner saw, but, of course, dared not call attention to the act, in the presence of the third personage who stood at her elbow. The minister decamped; leaving his own letter—one of no importance— upon the table."

"Here, then," said Dupin to me, "you have precisely what you demand to make the ascendancy complete—the robber's knowledge of the loser's knowledge of the robber."

"Yes," replied the Prefect; "and the power thus attained has, for some months past, been wielded, for political purposes, to a very dangerous extent. The personage robbed is more thoroughly convinced, every day, of the necessity of reclaiming her letter. But this, of course, cannot be done openly. In fine, driven to despair, she has committed the matter to me."

"Than whom," said Dupin, amid a perfect whirlwind of smoke, "no more sagacious agent could, I suppose, be desired, or even imagined."

"You flatter me," replied the Prefect; "but it is possible that some such opinion may have been entertained."

"It is clear," said I, "as you observe, that the letter is still in possession of the minister; since it is this possession, and not any employment of the letter, which bestows the power. With the employment the power departs."

"True," said G.; "and upon this conviction I proceeded. My first care was to make thorough search of the minister's hotel; and here my chief embarrassment lay in the necessity of searching without his knowledge. Beyond all things, I have been warned of the danger which would result from giving him reason to suspect our design."

"But," said I, "you are quite au fait in these investigations. The Parisian police have done this thing often before."

"O yes; and for this reason I did not despair. The habits of the minister gave me, too, a great advantage. He is frequently absent from home all night. His servants are by no means numerous. They sleep at a distance from their master's apartment, and, being chiefly Neapolitans, are readily made drunk. I have keys, as you know, with which I can open any chamber or cabinet in Paris. For three months a night has not passed, during the greater part of which I have not been engaged, personally, in ransacking the D— Hotel. My honor is interested, and, to mention a great secret, the reward is enormous. So I did not abandon the search until I had become fully satisfied that the thief is a more astute man than myself. I fancy that I have investigated every nook and corner of the premises in which it is possible that the paper can be concealed."

"But is it not possible," I suggested, "that although the letter may be in possession of the minister, as it unquestionably is, he may have concealed it elsewhere than upon his own premises?"

"This is barely possible," said Dupin. "The present peculiar condition of affairs at court, and especially of those intrigues in which D— is known to be involved, would render the instant availability of the document—its susceptibility of being produced at a moment's notice—a point of nearly equal importance with its possession."

"Its susceptibility of being produced?" said I.

"That is to say, of being destroyed," said Dupin.

"True," I observed; "the paper is clearly then upon the premises. As for its being upon the person of the minister, we may consider that as out of the question."

"Entirely," said the Prefect. "He has been twice waylaid, as if by footpads, and his person rigorously searched under my own inspection."

"You might have spared yourself this trouble," said Dupin. "D—, I presume, is not altogether a fool, and, if not, must have anticipated these waylayings, as a matter of course."

"Not altogether a fool," said G., "but then he's a poet, which I take to be only one remove from a fool."

"True," said Dupin, after a long and thoughtful whiff from his meerschaum, "although I have been guilty of certain doggerel myself."

"Suppose you detail," said I, "the particulars of your search."

"Why the fact is, we took our time, and we searched every where. I have had long experience in these affairs. I took the entire building, room by room; devoting the nights of a whole week to each. We examined, first, the furniture of each apartment. We opened every possible drawer; and I presume you know that, to a properly trained police agent, such a thing as a secret drawer is impossible. Any man is a dolt who permits a 'secret' drawer to escape him in a search of this kind. The thing is so plain. There is a certain amount of bulk—of space—to be accounted for in every cabinet. Then we have accurate rules. The fiftieth part of a line could not escape us. After the cabinets we took the chairs. The cushions we probed with the fine long needles you have seen me employ. From the tables we removed the tops."

"Why so?"

"Sometimes the top of a table, or other similarly arranged piece of furniture, is removed by the person wishing to conceal an article; then the leg is excavated, the article deposited within the cavity, and the top replaced. The bottoms and tops of bedposts are employed in the same way."

"But could not the cavity be detected by sounding?" I asked.

"By no means, if, when the article is deposited, a sufficient wadding of cotton be placed around it. Besides, in our case, we were obliged to proceed without noise."

"But you could not have removed—you could not have taken to pieces all articles of furniture in which it would have been possible to make a deposit in the manner you mention. A letter may be compressed into a thin spiral roll, not differing much in shape or bulk from a large knitting-needle, and in this form it might be inserted into the rung of a chair, for example. You did not take to pieces all the chairs?"

"Certainly not; but we did better—we examined the rungs of every chair in the hotel, and, indeed the jointings of every description of furniture, by the aid of a most powerful microscope. Had there been any traces of recent disturbance we should not have failed to detect it instantly. A single grain of gimlet-dust, for example, would have been as obvious as an apple. Any disorder in the glueing—any unusual gaping in the joints—would have sufficed to insure detection."

"I presume you looked to the mirrors, between the boards and the plates, and you probed the beds and the bed-clothes, as well as the curtains and carpets."

"That of course; and when we had absolutely completed every particle of the furniture in this way, then we examined the house itself. We divided its entire surface into compartments, which we numbered, so that none might be missed; then we scrutinized each individual square inch throughout the premises, including the two houses immediately adjoining, with the microscope, as before."

"The two houses adjoining!" I exclaimed; "you must have had a great deal of trouble."

"We had; but the reward offered is prodigious!"

"You include the grounds about the houses?"

"All the grounds are paved with brick. They gave us comparatively little trouble. We examined the moss between the bricks, and found it undisturbed."

"You looked among D—'s papers, of course, and into the books of the library?"

"Certainly; we opened every package and parcel; we not only opened every book, but we turned over every leaf in each volume, not contenting ourselves with a mere shake, according to the fashion of some of our police officers. We also measured the thickness of every book-cover, with the most accurate admeasurement, and applied to each the most jealous scrutiny of the microscope. Had any of the bindings been recently meddled with, it would have been utterly impossible that the fact should have escaped observation. Some five or six volumes, just from the hands of the binder, we carefully probed, longitudinally, with the needles."

"You explored the floors beneath the carpets?"

"Beyond doubt. We removed every carpet, and examined the boards with the microscope."

"And the paper on the walls?"

"Yes."

"You looked into the cellars?"

"We did."

"Then," I said, "you have been making a miscalculation, and the letter is not upon the premises, as you suppose."

"I fear you are right there," said the Prefect. "And now, Dupin, what would you advise me to do?"

"To make a thorough re-search of the premises."

"That is absolutely needless," replied G—. "I am not more sure that I breathe than I am that the letter is not at the Hotel."

"I have no better advice to give you," said Dupin. "You have, of course, an accurate description of the letter?"

"Oh yes!"—And here the Prefect, producing a memorandum-book proceeded to read aloud a minute account of the internal, and especially of the external appearance of the missing document. Soon after finishing the perusal of this description, he took his departure, more entirely depressed in spirits than I had ever known the good gentleman before. In about a month afterwards he paid us another visit, and found us occupied very nearly as before. He took a pipe and a chair and entered into some ordinary conversation. At length I said,—

"Well, but G—, what of the purloined letter? I presume you have at last made up your mind that there is no such thing as overreaching the Minister?"

"Confound him, say I—yes; I made the re-examination, however, as

Dupin suggested—but it was all labor lost, as I knew it would be."

"How much was the reward offered, did you say?" asked Dupin.

"Why, a very great deal—a very liberal reward—I don't like to say how much, precisely; but one thing I will say, that I wouldn't mind giving my individual check for fifty thousand francs to any one who could obtain me that letter. The fact is, it is becoming of more and more importance every day; and the reward has been lately doubled. If it were trebled, however, I could do no more than I have done."

"Why, yes," said Dupin, drawlingly, between the whiffs of his meerschaum, "I really—think, G—, you have not exerted yourself—to the utmost in this matter. You might—do a little more, I think, eh?"

"How?—in what way?"

"Why—puff, puff—you might—puff, puff—employ counsel in the matter, eh?—puff, puff, puff. Do you remember the story they tell of Abernethy?"

"No; hang Abernethy!"

"To be sure! Hang him and welcome. But, once upon a time, a certain rich miser conceived the design of spunging upon this Abernethy for a medical opinion. Getting up, for this purpose, an ordinary conversation in a private company, he insinuated his case to the physician, as that of an imaginary individual.

"'We will suppose,' said the miser, 'that his symptoms are such and such; now, doctor, what would you have directed him to take?'

"'Take!' said Abernethy, 'why, take advice, to be sure.'"

"But," said the Prefect, a little discomposed, "I am perfectly willing to take advice, and to pay for it. I would really give fifty thousand francs to any one who would aid me in the matter."

"In that case," replied Dupin, opening a drawer, and producing a check-book, "you may as well fill me up a check for the amount mentioned. When you have signed it, I will hand you the letter."

I was astounded. The Prefect appeared absolutely thunder-stricken. For some minutes he remained speechless and motionless, looking incredulously at my friend with open mouth, and eyes that seemed starting from their sockets; then, apparently recovering himself in some measure, he seized a pen, and after several pauses and vacant stares, finally filled up and signed a check for fifty thousand francs, and handed it across the table to Dupin. The latter examined it carefully and deposited it in his pocket-book; then, unlocking an escritoire, took thence a letter and gave it to the Prefect. This functionary grasped it in a perfect agony of joy, opened it with a trembling hand, cast a rapid glance at its contents, and then, scrambling and struggling to the door, rushed at length unceremoniously from the room and from the house, without having uttered a syllable since

Dupin had requested him to fill up the check.

When he had gone, my friend entered into some explanations.

"The Parisian police," he said, "are exceedingly able in their way. They are persevering, ingenious, cunning, and thoroughly versed in the knowledge which their duties seem chiefly to demand. Thus, when G— detailed to us his mode of searching the premises at the Hotel D—, I felt entire confidence in his having made a satisfactory investigation—so far as his labors extended."

"So far as his labors extended?" said I.

"Yes," said Dupin. "The measures adopted were not only the best of their kind, but carried out to absolute perfection. Had the letter been deposited within the range of their search, these fellows would, beyond a question, have found it."

I merely laughed—but he seemed quite serious in all that he said.

"The measures, then," he continued, "were good in their kind, and well executed; their defect lay in their being inapplicable to the case, and to the man. A certain set of highly ingenious resources are, with the Prefect, a sort of Procrustean bed, to which he forcibly adapts his designs. But he perpetually errs by being too deep or too shallow, for the matter in hand; and many a schoolboy is a better reasoner than he. I knew one about eight years of age, whose success at guessing in the game of 'even and odd' attracted universal admiration. This game is simple, and is played with marbles. One player holds in his hand a number of these toys, and demands of another whether that number is even or odd. If the guess is right, the guesser wins one; if wrong, he loses one. The boy to whom I allude won all the marbles of the school. Of course he had some principle of guessing; and this lay in mere observation and admeasurement of the astuteness of his opponents. For example, an arrant simpleton is his opponent, and, holding up his closed hand, asks, 'are they even or odd?' Our schoolboy replies, 'odd,' and loses; but upon the second trial he wins, for he then says to himself, 'the simpleton had them even upon the first trial, and his amount of cunning is just sufficient to make him have them odd upon the second; I will therefore guess odd;'—he guesses odd, and wins. Now, with a simpleton a degree above the first, he would have reasoned thus: 'This fellow finds that in the first instance I guessed odd, and, in the second, he will propose to himself, upon the first impulse, a simple variation from even to odd, as did the first simpleton; but then a second thought will suggest that this is too simple a variation, and finally he will decide upon putting it even as before. I will therefore guess even;'—he guesses even, and wins. Now this mode of reasoning in the schoolboy, whom his fellows termed 'lucky,'—what, in its last analysis, is it?"

"It is merely," I said, "an identification of the reasoner's intellect with that of his opponent."

"It is," said Dupin; "and, upon inquiring of the boy by what means he effected the thorough identification in which his success consisted, I received answer as follows: 'When I wish to find out how wise, or how stupid, or how good, or how wicked is any one, or what are his thoughts at the moment, I fashion the expression of my face, as accurately as possible, in accordance with the expression of his, and then wait to see what thoughts or sentiments arise in my mind or heart, as if to match or correspond with the expression.' This response of the schoolboy lies at the bottom of all the spurious profundity which has been attributed to Rochefoucault, to La Bougive, to Machiavelli, and to Campanella."

"And the identification," I said, "of the reasoner's intellect with that of his opponent, depends, if I understand you aright, upon the accuracy with which the opponent's intellect is admeasured."

"For its practical value it depends upon this," replied Dupin; "and the Prefect and his cohort fail so frequently, first, by default of this identification, and, secondly, by ill-admeasurement, or rather through non-admeasurement, of the intellect with which they are engaged. They consider only their own ideas of ingenuity; and, in searching for anything hidden, advert only to the modes in which they would have hidden it. They are right in this much—that their own ingenuity is a faithful representative of that of the mass; but when the cunning of the individual felon is diverse in character from their own, the felon foils them, of course. This always happens when it is above their own, and very usually when it is below. They have no variation of principle in their investigations; at best, when urged by some unusual emergency—by some extraordinary reward—they extend or exaggerate their old modes of practice, without touching their principles. What, for example, in this case of D—, has been done to vary the principle of action? What is all this boring, and probing, and sounding, and scrutinizing with the microscope and dividing the surface of the building into registered square inches—what is it all but an exaggeration of the application of the one principle or set of principles of search, which are based upon the one set of notions regarding human ingenuity, to which the Prefect, in the long routine of his duty, has been accustomed? Do you not see he has taken it for granted that all men proceed to conceal a letter,—not exactly in a gimlet hole bored in a chair-leg—but, at least, in some out-of-the-way hole or corner suggested by the same tenor of thought which would urge a man to secrete a letter in a gimlet-hole bored in a chair-leg? And do you not see also, that such recherchés nooks for concealment are adapted only for ordinary occasions, and would be adopted only by ordinary intellects; for, in all cases of concealment, a disposal of the article concealed—a disposal of it in this recherché manner,—is, in the very first instance, presumable and presumed; and thus its discovery depends, not at all upon the acumen, but altogether upon the mere care, patience, and determination of the seekers; and where the case is of importance—or, what amounts to the same thing in the policial eyes, when the reward is of magnitude,—the qualities in question have never been known to fail. You will now understand what I meant in suggesting that, had the purloined letter been hidden any where within the limits of the Prefect's examination—in other words, had the principle of its concealment been comprehended within the principles of the Prefect—its discovery would have been a matter altogether beyond question. This functionary, however, has been thoroughly mystified; and the remote source of his defeat lies in the supposition that the Minister is a fool, because he has acquired renown as a poet. All fools are poets; this the Prefect feels; and he is merely guilty of a non distributio medii in thence inferring that all poets are fools."

"But is this really the poet?" I asked. "There are two brothers, I know; and both have attained reputation in letters. The Minister I believe has written learnedly on the Differential Calculus. He is a mathematician, and no poet."

"You are mistaken; I know him well; he is both. As poet and mathematician, he would reason well; as mere mathematician, he could not have reasoned at all, and thus would have been at the mercy of the Prefect."

"You surprise me," I said, "by these opinions, which have been contradicted by the voice of the world. You do not mean to set at naught the well-digested idea of centuries. The mathematical reason has long been regarded as the reason par excellence."

"'Il y a à parièr,'" replied Dupin, quoting from Chamfort, "'que toute idée publique, toute convention reçue est une sottise, car elle a convenue au plus grand nombre.' The mathematicians, I grant you, have done their best to promulgate the popular error to which you allude, and which is none the less an error for its promulgation as truth. With an art worthy a better cause, for example, they have insinuated the term 'analysis' into application to algebra. The French are the originators of this particular deception; but if a term is of any importance—if words derive any value from applicability—then 'analysis' conveys 'algebra' about as much as, in Latin, 'ambitus' implies 'ambition,' 'religio' 'religion,' or 'homines honesti,' a set of honorablemen."

"You have a quarrel on hand, I see," said I, "with some of the algebraists of Paris; but proceed."

"I dispute the availability, and thus the value, of that reason which is cultivated in any especial form other than the abstractly logical. I dispute, in particular, the reason educed by mathematical study. The mathematics are the science of form and quantity; mathematical reasoning is merely logic applied to observation upon form and quantity. The great error lies in supposing that even the truths of what is called pure algebra, are abstract or general truths. And this error is so egregious that I am confounded at the universality with which it has been received. Mathematical axioms are not axioms of general truth. What is true of relation—of form and quantity—is often grossly false in regard to morals, for example. In this latter science it is very usually untrue that the aggregated parts are equal to the whole. In chemistry also the axiom fails. In the consideration of motive it fails; for two motives, each of a given value, have not, necessarily, a value when united, equal to the sum of their values apart. There are numerous other mathematical truths which are only truths within the limits of relation. But the mathematician argues, from his finite truths, through habit, as if they were of an absolutely general applicability—as the world indeed imagines them to be. Bryant, in his very learned 'Mythology,' mentions an analogous source of error, when he says that 'although the Pagan fables are not believed, yet we forget ourselves continually, and make inferences from them as existing realities.' With the algebraists, however, who are Pagans themselves, the 'Pagan fables' are believed, and the inferences are made, not so much through lapse of memory, as through an unaccountable addling of the brains. In short, I never yet encountered the mere mathematician who could be trusted out of equal roots, or one who did not clandestinely hold it as a point of his faith that $x2+px$ was absolutely and unconditionally equal to q. Say to one of these gentlemen, by way of experiment, if you please, that you believe occasions may occur where $x2+px$ is not altogether equal to q, and, having made him understand what you mean, get out of his reach as speedily as convenient, for, beyond doubt, he will endeavor to knock you down.

"I mean to say," continued Dupin, while I merely laughed at his last observations, "that if the Minister had been no more than a mathematician, the Prefect would have been under no necessity of giving me this check. I know him, however, as both mathematician and poet, and my measures were adapted to his capacity, with reference to the circumstances by which he was surrounded. I knew him as a courtier, too, and as a bold intriguant. Such a man, I considered, could not fail to be aware of the ordinary policial modes of action. He could not have failed to anticipate— and events have proved that he did not fail to anticipate—the waylayings to which he was subjected. He must have foreseen, I reflected, the secret investigations of his premises. His frequent absences from home at night, which were hailed by the Prefect as certain aids to his success, I regarded only as ruses, to afford opportunity for thorough search to the police, and thus the sooner to impress them with the conviction to which G—, in fact, did finally arrive—the conviction that the letter was not upon the premises. I felt, also, that the whole train of thought, which I was at some pains in detailing to you just now, concerning the invariable principle of policial action in searches for articles concealed—I felt that this whole train of thought would necessarily pass through the mind of the Minister. It would imperatively lead him to despise all the ordinary nooks of concealment. He could not, I reflected, be so weak as not to see that the most intricate and remote recess of his hotel would be as open as his commonest closets to the eyes, to the probes, to the gimlets, and to the microscopes of the Prefect. I saw, in fine, that he would be driven, as a matter of course, to simplicity, if not deliberately induced to it as a matter of choice. You will remember, perhaps, how desperately the Prefect laughed when I suggested, upon our first interview, that it was just possible this mystery troubled him so much on account of its being so very self-evident."

"Yes," said I, "I remember his merriment well. I really thought he would have fallen into convulsions."

"The material world," continued Dupin, "abounds with very strict analogies to the immaterial; and thus some color of truth has been given to the rhetorical dogma, that metaphor, or simile, may be made to strengthen an argument, as well as to embellish a description. The principle of the vis inertiæ, for example, seems to be identical in physics and metaphysics. It is not more true in the former, that a large body is with more difficulty set in motion than a smaller one, and that its subsequent momentum is commensurate with this difficulty, than it is, in the latter, that intellects of the vaster capacity, while more forcible, more constant, and more eventful in their movements than those of inferior grade, are yet the less readily moved, and more embarrassed and full of hesitation in the first few steps of their progress. Again: have you ever noticed which of the street signs, over the shop-doors, are the most attractive of attention?"

"I have never given the matter a thought," I said.

"There is a game of puzzles," he resumed, "which is played upon a map. One party playing requires another to find a given word—the name of town, river, state or empire—any word, in short, upon the motley and perplexed surface of the chart. A novice in the game generally seeks to embarrass his opponents by giving them the most minutely lettered names; but the adept selects such words as stretch, in large characters, from one end of the chart to the other. These, like the over-largely lettered signs and placards of the street, escape observation by dint of being excessively obvious; and here the physical oversight is precisely analogous with the moral inapprehension by which the intellect suffers to pass unnoticed those considerations which are too obtrusively and too palpably self-evident. But this is a point, it appears, somewhat above or beneath the understanding of the Prefect. He never once thought it probable, or possible, that the Minister had deposited the letter immediately beneath the nose of the whole world, by way of best preventing any portion of that world from perceiving it.

"But the more I reflected upon the daring, dashing, and discriminating ingenuity of D—; upon the fact that the document must always have been at hand, if he intended to use it to good purpose; and upon the decisive evidence, obtained by the Prefect, that it was not hidden within the limits of that dignitary's ordinary search—the more satisfied I became that, to conceal this letter, the Minister had resorted to the comprehensive and sagacious expedient of not attempting to conceal it at all.

"Full of these ideas, I prepared myself with a pair of green spectacles, and called one fine morning, quite by accident, at the Ministerial hotel. I found D— at home, yawning, lounging, and dawdling, as usual, and pretending to be in the last extremity of ennui. He is, perhaps, the most really energetic human being now alive—but that is only when nobody sees him.

"To be even with him, I complained of my weak eyes, and lamented the necessity of the spectacles, under cover of which I cautiously and thoroughly surveyed the whole apartment, while seemingly intent only upon the conversation of my host.

"I paid especial attention to a large writing-table near which he sat, and upon which lay confusedly, some miscellaneous letters and other papers, with one or two musical instruments and a few books. Here, however, after a long and very deliberate scrutiny, I saw nothing to excite particular suspicion.

"At length my eyes, in going the circuit of the room, fell upon a trumpery fillagree card-rack of pasteboard, that hung dangling by a dirty blue ribbon, from a little brass knob just beneath the middle of the mantel-piece. In this rack, which had three or four compartments, were five or six visiting cards and a solitary letter. This last was much soiled and crumpled. It was torn nearly in two, across the middle—as if a design, in the first instance, to tear it entirely up as worthless, had been altered, or stayed, in the second. It had a large black seal, bearing the D— cipher very conspicuously, and was addressed, in a diminutive female hand, to D—, the minister, himself. It was thrust carelessly, and even, as it seemed, contemptuously, into one of the uppermost divisions of the rack.

"No sooner had I glanced at this letter, than I concluded it to be that of which I was in search. To be sure, it was, to all appearance, radically different from the one of which the Prefect had read us so minute a description. Here the seal was large and black, with the D— cipher; there it was small and red, with the ducal arms of the S— family. Here, the address, to the

Minister, diminutive and feminine; there the superscription, to a certain royal personage, was markedly bold and decided; the size alone formed a point of correspondence. But, then, the radicalness of these differences, which was excessive; the dirt; the soiled and torn condition of the paper, so inconsistent with the true methodical habits of D——, and so suggestive of a design to delude the beholder into an idea of the worthlessness of the document; these things, together with the hyper-obtrusive situation of this document, full in the view of every visiter, and thus exactly in accordance with the conclusions to which I had previously arrived; these things, I say, were strongly corroborative of suspicion, in one who came with the intention to suspect.

"I protracted my visit as long as possible, and, while I maintained a most animated discussion with the Minister upon a topic which I knew well had never failed to interest and excite him, I kept my attention really riveted upon the letter. In this examination, I committed to memory its external appearance and arrangement in the rack; and also fell, at length, upon a discovery which set at rest whatever trivial doubt I might have entertained. In scrutinizing the edges of the paper, I observed them to be more chafed than seemed necessary. They presented the broken appearance which is manifested when a stiff paper, having been once folded and pressed with a folder, is refolded in a reversed direction, in the same creases or edges which had formed the original fold. This discovery was sufficient. It was clear to me that the letter had been turned, as a glove, inside out, re-directed, and re-sealed. I bade the Minister good morning, and took my departure at once, leaving a gold snuff-box upon the table.

"The next morning I called for the snuff-box, when we resumed, quite eagerly, the conversation of the preceding day. While thus engaged, however, a loud report, as if of a pistol, was heard immediately beneath the windows of the hotel, and was succeeded by a series of fearful screams, and the shoutings of a terrified mob. D—— rushed to a casement, threw it open, and looked out. In the meantime, I stepped to the card-rack, took the letter, put it in my pocket, and replaced it by a fac-simile, (so far as regards externals,) which I had carefully prepared at my lodgings—imitating the D—— cipher, very readily, by means of a seal formed of bread.

"The disturbance in the street had been occasioned by the frantic behavior of a man with a musket. He had fired it among a crowd of women and children. It proved, however, to have been without ball, and the fellow was suffered to go his way as a lunatic or a drunkard. When he had gone, D—— came from the window, whither I had followed him immediately upon securing the object in view. Soon afterwards I bade him farewell. The pretended lunatic was a man in my own pay."

"But what purpose had you," I asked, "in replacing the letter by a fac-simile? Would it not have been better, at the first visit, to have seized it openly, and departed?"

"D—," replied Dupin, "is a desperate man, and a man of nerve. His hotel, too, is not without attendants devoted to his interests. Had I made the wild attempt you suggest, I might never have left the Ministerial presence alive. The good people of Paris might have heard of me no more. But I had an object apart from these considerations. You know my political prepossessions. In this matter, I act as a partisan of the lady concerned. For eighteen months the Minister has had her in his power. She has now him in hers—since, being unaware that the letter is not in his possession, he will proceed with his exactions as if it was. Thus will he inevitably commit himself, at once, to his political destruction. His downfall, too, will not be more precipitate than awkward. It is all very well to talk about the facilis descensus Averni; but in all kinds of climbing, as Catalani said of singing, it is far more easy to get up than to come down. In the present instance I have no sympathy—at least no pity—for him who descends. He is that monstrum horrendum, an unprincipled man of genius. I confess, however, that I should like very well to know the precise character of his thoughts, when, being defied by her whom the Prefect terms 'a certain personage' he is reduced to opening the letter which I left for him in the card-rack."

"How? Did you put any thing particular in it?"

"Why—it did not seem altogether right to leave the interior blank—that would have been insulting. D—, at Vienna once, did me an evil turn, which I told him, quite good-humoredly, that I should remember. So, as I knew he would feel some curiosity in regard to the identity of the person who had outwitted him, I thought it a pity not to give him a clue. He is well acquainted with my MS., and I just copied into the middle of the blank sheet the words—

"'— — Un dessein si funeste, S'il n'est digne d'Atrée, est digne de Thyeste. They are to be found in Crebillon's 'Atrée.'"

A SCANDAL IN BOHEMIA (1891)

SIR ARTHUR CONAN DOYLE (1859-1930)

The pipe; the deerstalker hat; the magnifying glass; the aquiline nose; the bumbling companion hanging on his every deduction; the self-congratulatory chuckle at the conclusion of a case; the cocaine syringe: these are the hallmarks of the most popular fictional detective—hell, of the most popular literary hero (take that, Harry Potter!)—England has ever known: Sherlock Holmes!

Far more popular than Poe's FRANCOPHONE C. August Dupin, the quintessentially British "consulting detective" created by Sir Arthur Conan Doyle captured the public imagination <u>almost</u> from the moment of his conception, spawning 56 short stories and four novels between 1187-1927. And yet, there is little—aside from Doyle's voice, an ocean, and 46 years—that initially separated Holmes from Dupin: both are RATIOCINATORS whose relatively "normal" sidekicks narrate their "superheroic" intellectual exercises; both operate outside (but with) the law proper; both are, frankly, a bit pompous and egocentric. Why, then, did Holmes become so popular that—when Doyle grew tired of writing the character and killed him off (in 1893)—the reading public in Britain all but boycotted Doyle's subsequent stories until he brought back their beloved fictional/national hero?

It is, as Dupin might say, a Gordian poser, to be sure. It's not as if Detective Fiction had ceased to exist between Poe and Doyle: writers like Wilkie Collins, Mary Elizabeth Braddon, Valeria Woodville, and Fergus Hume all helped formalize the form that would formally be known as "Detective Fiction" in the years leading up to Holmes' debut in A Study In Scarlet *(first published in* Beeton's Christmas Annual *magazine, 1887). In short, the mystery genre endured, smouldering, but had not yet caught fire. Culture, as ever, had shifted since Poe, from the ROMANTIC/ GOTHIC periods to the Victorian-inspired AGE OF REALISM, so public sensibilities might account for some of Holmes' eventual popularity. Doyle's English readership was, of course, rather distinct from Poe's largely American audience; broad cultural differences might be considered influential in Doyle's success (Victorian repression, (post)COLONIALISM, women's SUFFRAGE, and so forth). But one particular historical event— chronologically coincidental with Doyle's consulting detective—may have created a cultural "need" for a master RATIOCINATOR and mystery solver: the Whitechapel Murders.*

From 1888-1891 a series of brutal murders (five "canonical" and a half-dozen possible copycats) in the cheap streets of London spawned conspiracy theories and a media frenzy: Jack the Ripper—the Western world's first "serial killer"—terrorized public imagination. A confluence of factors contributed to the popular sensationalism of the murders: the targets were primarily prostitutes (sex!); the victims' throats were slashed (violence!) and their genitalia mutilated (morality!) or reproductive organs "surgically" removed (science!); and the crimes were limited to the slums of the East End (class-war!). Scotland Yard was baffled— even implicated—and London's growing newspaper industry fed public anxiety: a letter "from Hell" was even published, allegedly from the Ripper himself. The serial killer also known as "Leather Apron" or "The Whitechapel Murderer" was never caught, but Jews, physicians, butchers, syphilitic royalty—even Doyle himself—were popularly accused of the atrocities over the years.

What the English reading public, in 1888, needed, was a hero. A "modern" Victorian hero who could solve unsolvable mysteries, who would stop the insanity of GOTHIC horror haunting their nascent AGE OF REALISM: what they needed, in short, was a truly English RATIOCINATOR.

Fortunately, he had already arrived at 221B Baker Street...via Beeton's Christmas Annual, *of all places.*

I

To Sherlock Holmes she is always the woman. I have seldom heard him mention her under any other name. In his eyes she eclipses and predominates the whole of her sex. It was not that he felt any emotion akin to love for Irene Adler. All emotions, and that one particularly, were abhorrent to his cold, precise, but admirably balanced mind. He was, I take it, the most perfect reasoning and observing machine that the world has seen; but, as a lover, he would have placed himself in a false position. He never spoke of the softer passions, save with a gibe and a sneer. They were admirable things for the observer—excellent for drawing the veil from men's motives and actions. But for the trained reasoner to admit such intrusions into his own delicate and finely adjusted temperament was to introduce a distracting factor which might throw a doubt upon all his mental results. Grit in a sensitive instrument, or a crack in one of his own high-power lenses, would not be more disturbing than a strong emotion in a nature such as his. And yet there was but one woman to him, and that woman was the late Irene Adler, of dubious and questionable memory.

I had seen little of Holmes lately. My marriage had drifted us away from each other. My own complete happiness, and the home-centred interests which rise up around the man who first finds himself master of his own establishment, were sufficient to absorb all my attention; while Holmes, who loathed every form of society with his whole Bohemian soul, remained in our lodgings in Baker Street, buried among his old books, and alternating from week to week between cocaine and ambition, the drowsiness of the drug, and the fierce energy of his own keen nature. He was still, as ever, deeply attracted by the study of crime, and occupied his immense faculties and extraordinary powers of observation in following out those clues, and clearing up those mysteries, which had been abandoned as hopeless by the official police. From time to time I heard some vague account of his doings: of his summons to Odessa in the case of the Trepoff murder, of his clearing up of the singular tragedy of the Atkinson brothers at Trincomalee, and finally of the mission which he had accomplished so delicately and successfully for the reigning family of Holland. Beyond these signs of his activity, however, which I merely shared with all the readers of the daily press, I knew little of my former friend and companion.

One night—it was on the 20th of March, 1888—I was returning from a journey to a patient (for I had now returned to civil practice), when my way led me through Baker Street. As I passed the well-remembered door, which must always be associated in my mind with my wooing, and with the dark incidents of the Study in Scarlet, I was seized with a keen desire to see Holmes again, and to know how he was employing his extraordinary powers. His rooms were brilliantly lit, and, even as I looked up, I saw his tall, spare figure pass twice in a dark silhouette against the blind. He was pacing the room swiftly, eagerly, with his head sunk upon his chest and his hands clasped behind him. To me, who knew his every mood and habit, his attitude and manner told their own story. He was at work again. He had arisen out of his drug-created dreams, and was hot upon the scent of some new problem. I rang the bell, and was shown up to the chamber which had formerly been in part my own.

His manner was not effusive. It seldom was; but he was glad, I think, to see me. With hardly a word spoken, but with a kindly eye, he waved me to an arm-chair, threw across his case of cigars, and indicated a spirit case and a gasogene in the corner. Then he stood before the fire, and looked me over in his singular introspective fashion.

"Wedlock suits you," he remarked. "I think, Watson, that you have put on seven and a half pounds since I saw you."

"Seven!" I answered.

"Indeed, I should have thought a little more. Just a trifle more, I fancy, Watson. And in practice again, I observe. You did not tell me that you intended to go into harness."

"Then, how do you know?"

"I see it, I deduce it. How do I know that you have been getting yourself very wet lately, and that you have a most clumsy and careless servant girl?"

"My dear Holmes," said I, "this is too much. You would certainly have been burned, had you lived a few centuries ago. It is true that I had a country walk on Thursday and came home in a dreadful mess; but, as I have changed my clothes, I can't imagine how you deduce it. As to Mary Jane, she is incorrigible, and my wife has given her notice; but there, again, I fail to see how you work it out."

He chuckled to himself and rubbed his long, nervous hands together.

"It is simplicity itself," said he; "my eyes tell me that on the inside of your left shoe, just where the firelight strikes it, the leather is scored by six almost parallel cuts. Obviously they have been caused by some one who has very carelessly scraped round the edges of the sole in order to remove crusted mud from it. Hence, you see, my double deduction that you had been out in vile weather, and that you had a particularly malignant boot-slitting specimen of the London slavey. As to your practice, if a gentleman walks into my rooms smelling of iodoform, with a black mark of nitrate of silver upon his right forefinger, and a bulge on the side of his top-hat to show where he has secreted his stethoscope, I must be dull, indeed, if I do not pronounce him to be an active member of the medical profession."

I could not help laughing at the ease with which he explained his process of deduction. "When I hear you give your reasons," I remarked, "the thing always appears to me to be so ridiculously simple that I could easily do it myself, though at each successive instance of your reasoning I am baffled, until you explain your process. And yet I believe that my eyes are as good as yours."

"Quite so," he answered, lighting a cigarette, and throwing himself down into an arm-chair. "You see, but you do not observe. The distinction is clear. For example, you have frequently seen the steps which lead up from the hall to this room."

"Frequently."

"How often?"

"Well, some hundreds of times."

"Then how many are there?"

"How many? I don't know."

"Quite so! You have not observed. And yet you have seen. That is just my point. Now, I know that there are seventeen steps, because I have both seen and observed. By-the-way, since you are interested in these little problems, and since you are good enough to chronicle one or two of my trifling experiences, you may be interested in this." He threw over a sheet of thick, pink-tinted note-paper which had been lying open upon the table. "It came by the last post," said he.

"Read it aloud."

The note was undated, and without either signature or address.

"There will call upon you to-night, at a quarter to eight o'clock," it said, "a gentleman who desires to consult you upon a matter of the very deepest moment. Your recent services to one of the royal houses of Europe have shown that you are one who may safely be trusted with matters which are of an importance which can hardly be exaggerated. This account of you we have from all quarters received. Be in your chamber then at that hour, and do not take it amiss if your visitor wear a mask."

"This is indeed a mystery," I remarked. "What do you imagine that it means?"

"I have no data yet. It is a capital mistake to theorize before one has data. Insensibly one begins to twist facts to suit theories, instead of theories to suit facts. But the note itself. What do you deduce from it?"

I carefully examined the writing, and the paper upon which it was written.

"The man who wrote it was presumably well to do," I remarked, endeavoring to imitate my companion's processes. "Such paper could not be bought under half a crown a packet. It is peculiarly strong and stiff."

"Peculiar—that is the very word," said Holmes. "It is not an English paper at all. Hold it up to the light."

I did so, and saw a large E with a small g, a P, and a large G with a small t woven into the texture of the paper.

"What do you make of that?" asked Holmes.

"The name of the maker, no doubt; or his monogram, rather."

"Not at all. The G with the small t stands for 'Gesellschaft,' which is the German for 'Company.' It is a customary contraction like our 'Co.' P, of course, stands for 'Papier.' Now for the Eg. Let us glance at our Continental Gazetteer." He took down a heavy brown volume from his shelves. "Eglow, Eglonitz—here we are, Egria. It is in a German-speaking country—in Bohemia, not far from Carlsbad. 'Remarkable as being the scene of the death of Wallenstein, and for its numerous glass-factories and paper-mills.' Ha, ha, my boy, what do you make of that?" His eyes sparkled, and he sent up a great blue triumphant cloud from his cigarette.

"The paper was made in Bohemia," I said.

"Precisely. And the man who wrote the note is a German. Do you note the peculiar construction of the sentence—'This account of you we have from all quarters received.' A Frenchman or Russian could not have written that. It is the German who is so uncourteous to his verbs. It only remains, therefore, to discover what is wanted by this German who writes upon Bohemian paper, and prefers wearing a mask to showing his face. And here he comes, if I am not mistaken, to resolve all our doubts."

As he spoke there was the sharp sound of horses' hoofs and grating wheels against the curb, followed by a sharp pull at the bell. Holmes whistled.

"A pair, by the sound," said he. "Yes," he continued, glancing out of the window. "A nice little brougham and a pair of beauties. A hundred and fifty guineas apiece. There's money in this case, Watson, if there is nothing else."

"I think that I had better go, Holmes."

"Not a bit, doctor. Stay where you are. I am lost without my Boswell. And this promises to be interesting. It would be a pity to miss it."

"But your client—"

"Never mind him. I may want your help, and so may he. Here he comes. Sit down in that arm-chair, doctor, and give us your best attention."

A slow and heavy step, which had been heard upon the stairs and in the passage, paused immediately outside the door. Then there was a loud and authoritative tap.

"Come in!" said Holmes.

A man entered who could hardly have been less than six feet six inches in height, with the chest and limbs of a Hercules. His dress was rich with a richness which would, in England, be looked upon as akin to bad taste. Heavy bands of Astrakhan were slashed across the sleeves and fronts of his double-breasted coat, while the deep blue cloak which was thrown over his shoulders was lined with flame-colored silk, and secured at the neck with a brooch which consisted of a single flaming beryl. Boots which extended half-way up his calves, and which were trimmed at the tops with rich brown fur, completed the impression of barbaric opulence which was suggested by his whole appearance. He carried a broad-brimmed hat in his hand, while he wore across the upper part of his face, extending down past the cheekbones, a black vizard mask, which he had apparently adjusted that very moment, for his hand was still raised to it as he entered. From the lower part of the face he appeared to be a man of strong character, with a thick, hanging lip, and a long, straight chin, suggestive of resolution pushed to the length of obstinacy.

"You had my note?" he asked, with a deep harsh voice and a strongly marked German accent. "I told you that I would call." He looked from one to the other of us, as if uncertain which to address.

"Pray take a seat," said Holmes. "This is my friend and colleague, Dr. Watson, who is occasionally good enough to help me in my cases. Whom have I the honor to address?"

"You may address me as the Count Von Kramm, a Bohemian nobleman. I understand that this gentleman, your friend, is a man of honor and discretion, whom I may trust with a matter of the most extreme importance. If not, I should much prefer to communicate with you alone."

I rose to go, but Holmes caught me by the wrist and pushed me back into my chair. "It is both, or none," said he. "You may say before this gentleman anything which you may say to me."

The count shrugged his broad shoulders. "Then I must begin," said he, "by binding you both to absolute secrecy for two years, at the end of that time the matter will be of no importance. At present it is not too much to say that it is of such weight it may have an influence upon European history."

"I promise," said Holmes.

"And I."

"You will excuse this mask," continued our strange visitor. "The august person who employs me wishes his agent to be unknown to you, and I may confess at once that the title by which I have just called myself is not exactly my own."

"I was aware of it," said Holmes, dryly.

"The circumstances are of great delicacy, and every precaution has to be taken to quench what might grow to be an immense scandal and seriously compromise one of the reigning families of Europe. To speak plainly, the matter implicates the great House of Ormstein, hereditary kings of Bohemia."

"I was also aware of that," murmured Holmes, settling himself down in his arm-chair and closing his eyes.

Our visitor glanced with some apparent surprise at the languid, lounging figure of the man who had been no doubt depicted to him as the most incisive reasoner and most energetic agent in Europe. Holmes slowly reopened his eyes and looked impatiently at his gigantic client.

"If your Majesty would condescend to state your case," he remarked, "I should be better able to advise you."

The man sprang from his chair and paced up and down the room in uncontrollable agitation. Then, with a gesture of desperation, he tore the mask from his face and hurled it upon the ground. "You are right," he cried; "I am the King. Why should I attempt to conceal it?"

"Why, indeed?" murmured Holmes. "Your Majesty had not spoken before I was aware that I was addressing Wilhelm Gottsreich Sigismond von Ormstein, Grand Duke of Cassel-Felstein, and hereditary King of Bohemia."

"But you can understand," said our strange visitor, sitting down once more and passing his hand over his high, white forehead, "you can understand that I am not accustomed to doing such business in my own person. Yet the matter was so delicate that I could not confide it to an agent without putting myself in his power. I have come incognito from Prague for the purpose of consulting you."

"Then, pray consult," said Holmes, shutting his eyes once more.

"The facts are briefly these: Some five years ago, during a lengthy visit to Warsaw, I made the acquaintance of the well-known adventuress, Irene Adler. The name is no doubt familiar to you."

"Kindly look her up in my index, doctor," murmured Holmes, without opening his eyes. For many years he had adopted a system of docketing all paragraphs concerning men and things, so that it was difficult to name a subject or a person on which he could not at once furnish information. In this case I found her biography sandwiched in between that of a Hebrew Rabbi and that of a staff-commander who had written a monograph upon the deep-sea fishes.

"Let me see!" said Holmes. "Hum! Born in New Jersey in the year 1858. Contralto—hum! La Scala, hum! Prima donna Imperial Opera of Warsaw—Yes! Retired from operatic stage—ha! Living in London—quite so! Your Majesty, as I understand, became entangled with this young person, wrote her some compromising letters, and is now desirous of getting those letters back."

"Precisely so. But how—"

"Was there a secret marriage?"

"None."

"No legal papers or certificates?"

"None."

"Then I fail to follow your Majesty. If this young person should produce her letters for blackmailing or other purposes, how is she to prove their authenticity?"

"There is the writing."

"Pooh, pooh! Forgery."

"My private note-paper."

"Stolen."

"My own seal."

"Imitated."

"My photograph."

"Bought."

"We were both in the photograph."

"Oh dear! That is very bad! Your Majesty has indeed committed an indiscretion."

"I was mad—insane."

"You have compromised yourself seriously."

"I was only Crown Prince then. I was young. I am but thirty now."

"It must be recovered."

"We have tried and failed."

"Your Majesty must pay. It must be bought."

"She will not sell."

"Stolen, then."

"Five attempts have been made. Twice burglars in my pay ransacked her house. Once we diverted her luggage when she travelled. Twice she has been waylaid. There has been no result."

"No sign of it?"

"Absolutely none."

Holmes laughed. "It is quite a pretty little problem," said he.

"But a very serious one to me," returned the King, reproachfully.

"Very, indeed. And what does she propose to do with the photograph?"

"To ruin me."

"But how?"

"I am about to be married."

"So I have heard."

"To Clotilde Lothman von Saxe-Meningen, second daughter of the King of Scandinavia. You may know the strict principles of her family. She is herself the very soul of delicacy. A shadow of a doubt as to my conduct would bring the matter to an end."

"And Irene Adler?"

"Threatens to send them the photograph. And she will do it. I know that she will do it. You do not know her, but she has a soul of steel. She has the face of the most beautiful of women, and the mind of the most resolute of men. Rather than I should marry another woman, there are no lengths to which she would not go—none."

"You are sure that she has not sent it yet?"

"I am sure."

"And why?"

"Because she has said that she would send it on the day when the betrothal was publicly proclaimed. That will be next Monday."

"Oh, then, we have three days yet," said Holmes, with a yawn. "That is very fortunate, as I have one or two matters of importance to look into just at present. Your Majesty will, of course, stay in London for the present?"

"Certainly. You will find me at the Langham, under the name of the Count Von Kramm."

"Then I shall drop you a line to let you know how we progress."

"Pray do so. I shall be all anxiety."

"Then, as to money?"

"You have carte blanche."

"Absolutely?"

"I tell you that I would give one of the provinces of my kingdom to have that photograph."

"And for present expenses?"

The king took a heavy chamois leather bag from under his cloak and laid it on the table.

"There are three hundred pounds in gold and seven hundred in notes," he said.

Holmes scribbled a receipt upon a sheet of his note-book and handed it to him.

"And mademoiselle's address?" he asked.

"Is Briony Lodge, Serpentine Avenue, St. John's Wood."

Holmes took a note of it. "One other question," said he. "Was the photograph a cabinet?"

"It was."

"Then, good-night, your Majesty, and I trust that we shall soon have some good news for you. And good-night, Watson," he added, as the wheels of the royal brougham rolled down the street. "If you will be good enough to call to-morrow afternoon, at three o'clock, I should like to chat this little matter over with you."

II

At three o'clock precisely I was at Baker Street, but Holmes had not yet returned. The landlady informed me that he had left the house shortly after eight o'clock in the morning. I sat down beside the fire, however, with the intention of awaiting him, however long he might be. I was already deeply interested in his inquiry, for, though it was surrounded by none of the grim and strange features which were associated with the two crimes which I have already recorded, still, the nature of the case and the exalted station of his client gave it a character of its own. Indeed, apart from the nature of the investigation which my friend had on hand, there was something in his masterly grasp of a situation, and his keen, incisive reasoning, which made it a pleasure to me to study his system of work, and to follow the quick, subtle methods by which he disentangled the most inextricable mysteries. So accustomed was I to his invariable success that the very possibility of his failing had ceased to enter into my head.

It was close upon four before the door opened, and a drunken-looking groom, ill-kempt and side-whiskered, with an inflamed face and disreputable clothes, walked into the room. Accustomed as I was to my friend's amazing powers in the use of disguises, I had to look three times before I was certain that it was indeed he. With a nod he vanished into the bedroom, whence he emerged in five minutes tweed-suited and respectable, as of old. Putting his hands into his pockets, he stretched out his legs in front of the fire, and laughed heartily for some minutes.

"Well, really!" he cried, and then he choked; and laughed again until he was obliged to lie back, limp and helpless, in the chair.

"What is it?"

"It's quite too funny. I am sure you could never guess how I employed my morning, or what I ended by doing."

"I can't imagine. I suppose that you have been watching the habits, and perhaps the house, of Miss Irene Adler."

"Quite so; but the sequel was rather unusual. I will tell you, however. I left the house a little after eight o'clock this morning, in the character of a groom out of work. There is a wonderful sympathy and freemasonry among horsey men. Be one of them, and you will know all that there is to know. I soon found Briony Lodge. It is a bijou villa, with a garden at the back, but built out in front right up to the road, two stories. Chubb lock to the door. Large sitting-room on the right side, well furnished, with long windows almost to the floor, and those preposterous English window fasteners which a child could open. Behind there was nothing remarkable, save that the passage window could be reached from the top of the coach-house. I walked round it and examined it closely from every point of view, but without noting anything else of interest.

"I then lounged down the street, and found, as I expected, that there was a mews in a lane which runs down by one wall of the garden. I lent the ostlers a hand in rubbing down their horses, and I received in exchange twopence, a glass of half-and-half, two fills of shag tobacco, and as much information as I could desire about Miss Adler, to say nothing of half a dozen other people in the neighborhood in whom I was not in the least interested, but whose biographies I was compelled to listen to."

"And what of Irene Adler?" I asked.

"Oh, she has turned all the men's heads down in that part. She is the daintiest thing under a bonnet on this planet. So say the Serpentine-mews, to a man. She lives quietly, sings at concerts, drives out at five every day, and returns at seven sharp for dinner. Seldom goes out at other times, except when she sings. Has only one male visitor, but a good deal of him. He is dark, handsome, and dashing, never calls less than once a day, and often twice. He is a Mr. Godfrey Norton, of the Inner Temple. See the advantages of a cabman as a confidant. They had driven him home a dozen times from Serpentine-mews, and knew all about him. When I had listened to all that they had to tell, I began to walk up and down near Briony Lodge once more, and to think over my plan of campaign.

"This Godfrey Norton was evidently an important factor in the matter. He was a lawyer. That sounded ominous. What was the relation between them, and what the object of his repeated visits? Was she his client, his friend, or his mistress? If the former, she had probably transferred the photograph to his keeping. If the latter, it was less likely. On the issue of this question depended whether I should continue my work at Briony Lodge, or turn my attention to the gentleman's chambers in the Temple. It was a delicate point, and it widened the field of my inquiry. I fear that I bore you with these details, but I have to let you see my little difficulties, if you are to understand the situation."

"I am following you closely," I answered.

"I was still balancing the matter in my mind, when a hansom cab drove up to Briony Lodge, and a gentleman sprang out. He was a remarkably handsome man, dark, aquiline, and mustached—evidently the man of whom I had heard. He appeared to be in a great hurry, shouted to the cabman to wait, and brushed past the maid who opened the door with the air of a man who was thoroughly at home.

"He was in the house about half an hour, and I could catch glimpses of him in the windows of the sitting-room, pacing up and down, talking excitedly, and waving his arms. Of her I could see nothing. Presently he emerged, looking even more flurried than before. As he stepped up to the cab, he pulled a gold watch from his pocket and looked at it earnestly. 'Drive like the devil,' he shouted, 'first to Gross & Hankey's in Regent Street, and then to the church of St. Monica in the Edgware Road. Half a guinea if you do it in twenty minutes!'

"Away they went, and I was just wondering whether I should not do well to follow them, when up the lane came a neat little landau, the coachman with his coat only half-buttoned, and his tie under his ear, while all the tags of his harness were sticking out of the buckles. It hadn't pulled up before she shot out of the hall door and into it. I only caught a glimpse of her at the moment, but she was a lovely woman, with a face that a man might die for.

"'The Church of St. Monica, John,' she cried, 'and half a sovereign if you reach it in twenty minutes.'

"This was quite too good to lose, Watson. I was just balancing whether I should run for it, or whether I should perch behind her landau, when a cab came through the street. The driver looked twice at such a shabby fare; but I jumped in before he could object. 'The Church of St. Monica,' said I, 'and half a sovereign if you reach it in twenty minutes.' It was twenty-five minutes to twelve, and of course it was clear enough what was in the wind.

"My cabby drove fast. I don't think I ever drove faster, but the others were there before us. The cab and the landau with their steaming horses were in front of the door when I arrived. I paid the man and hurried into the church. There was not a soul there save the two whom I had followed and a surpliced clergyman, who seemed to be expostulating with them. They were all three standing in a knot in front of the altar. I lounged up the side aisle like any other idler who has dropped into a church. Suddenly, to my surprise, the three at the altar faced round to me, and Godfrey Norton came running as hard as he could towards me."

"Thank God!" he cried. "You'll do. Come! Come!"

"What then?" I asked.

"Come, man, come, only three minutes, or it won't be legal."

"I was half-dragged up to the altar, and, before I knew where I was, I found myself mumbling responses which were whispered in my ear, and vouching for things of which I knew nothing, and generally assisting in the secure tying up of Irene Adler, spinster, to Godfrey Norton, bachelor. It was all done in an instant, and there was the gentleman thanking me on the one side and the lady on the other, while the clergyman beamed on me in front. It was the most preposterous position in which I ever found myself in my life, and it was the thought of it that started me laughing just now. It seems that there had been some informality about their license, that the clergyman absolutely refused to marry them without a witness of some sort, and that my lucky appearance saved the bridegroom from having to sally out into the streets in search of a best man. The bride gave me a sovereign, and I mean to wear it on my watch-chain in memory of the occasion."

"This is a very unexpected turn of affairs," said I; "and what then?"

"Well, I found my plans very seriously menaced. It looked as if the pair might take an immediate departure, and so necessitate very prompt and energetic measures on my part. At the church door, however, they separated, he driving back to the Temple, and she to her own house. 'I shall drive out in the park at five as usual,' she said, as she left him. I heard no more. They drove away in different directions, and I went off to make my own arrangements."

"Which are?"

"Some cold beef and a glass of beer," he answered, ringing the bell. "I have been too busy to think of food, and I am likely to be busier still this evening. By the way, doctor, I shall want your co-operation."

"I shall be delighted."

"You don't mind breaking the law?"

"Not in the least."

"Nor running a chance of arrest?"

"Not in a good cause."

"Oh, the cause is excellent!"

"Then I am your man."

"I was sure that I might rely on you."

"But what is it you wish?"

"When Mrs. Turner has brought in the tray I will make it clear to you. Now," he said, as he turned hungrily on the simple fare that our landlady had provided, "I must discuss it while I eat, for I have not much time. It is nearly five now. In two hours we must be on the scene of action. Miss Irene, or Madame, rather, returns from her drive at seven. We must be at Briony Lodge to meet her."

"And what then?"

"You must leave that to me. I have already arranged what is to occur. There is only one point on which I must insist. You must not interfere, come what may. You understand?"

"I am to be neutral?"

"To do nothing whatever. There will probably be some small unpleasantness. Do not join in it. It will end in my being conveyed into the house. Four or five minutes afterwards the sitting-room window will open. You are to station yourself close to that open window."

"Yes."

"You are to watch me, for I will be visible to you."

"Yes."

"And when I raise my hand—so—you will throw into the room what I give you to throw, and will, at the same time, raise the cry of fire. You quite follow me?"

"Entirely."

"It is nothing very formidable," he said, taking a long cigar-shaped roll from his pocket. "It is an ordinary plumber's smoke-rocket, fitted with a cap at either end to make it self-lighting. Your task is confined to that. When you raise your cry of fire, it will be taken up by quite a number of people. You may then walk to the end of the street, and I will rejoin you in ten minutes. I hope that I have made myself clear?"

"I am to remain neutral, to get near the window, to watch you, and, at the signal, to throw in this object, then to raise the cry of fire, and to wait you at the corner of the street."

"Precisely."

"Then you may entirely rely on me."

"That is excellent. I think, perhaps, it is almost time that I prepare for the new role I have to play."

He disappeared into his bedroom, and returned in a few minutes in the character of an amiable and simple-minded Nonconformist clergyman. His broad black hat, his baggy trousers, his white tie, his sympathetic smile, and general look of peering and benevolent curiosity were such as

Mr. John Hare alone could have equalled. It was not merely that Holmes changed his costume. His expression, his manner, his very soul seemed to vary with every fresh part that he assumed. The stage lost a fine actor, even as science lost an acute reasoner, when he became a specialist in crime.

It was a quarter past six when we left Baker Street, and it still wanted ten minutes to the hour when we found ourselves in Serpentine Avenue. It was already dusk, and the lamps were just being lighted as we paced up and down in front of Briony Lodge, waiting for the coming of its occupant. The house was just such as I had pictured it from Sherlock Holmes's succinct description, but the locality appeared to be less private that I expected. On the contrary, for a small street in a quiet neighborhood, it was remarkably animated. There was a group of shabbily-dressed men smoking and laughing in a corner, a scissors-grinder with his wheel, two guardsmen who were flirting with a nurse-girl, and several well-dressed young men who were lounging up and down with cigars in their mouths.

"You see," remarked Holmes, as we paced to and fro in front of the house, "this marriage rather simplifies matters. The photograph becomes a double-edged weapon now. The chances are that she would be as averse to its being seen by Mr. Godfrey Norton, as our client is to its coming to the eyes of his princess. Now the question is, where are we to find the photograph?"

"Where, indeed?"

"It is most unlikely that she carries it about with her. It is cabinet size. Too large for easy concealment about a woman's dress. She knows that the King is capable of having her waylaid and searched. Two attempts of the sort have already been made. We may take it, then, that she does not carry it about with her."

"Where, then?"

"Her banker or her lawyer. There is that double possibility. But I am inclined to think neither. Women are naturally secretive, and they like to do their own secreting. Why should she hand it over to any one else? She could trust her own guardianship, but she could not tell what indirect or political influence might be brought to bear upon a business man. Besides, remember that she had resolved to use it within a few days. It must be where she can lay her hands upon it. It must be in her own house."

"But it has twice been burgled."

"Pshaw! They did not know how to look."

"But how will you look?"

"I will not look."

"What then?"

"I will get her to show me."

"But she will refuse."

"She will not be able to. But I hear the rumble of wheels. It is her carriage. Now carry out my orders to the letter."

As he spoke the gleam of the side-lights of a carriage came round the curve of the avenue. It was a smart little landau which rattled up to the door of Briony Lodge. As it pulled up, one of the loafing men at the corner dashed forward to open the door in the hope of earning a copper, but was elbowed away by another loafer, who had rushed up with the same intention. A fierce quarrel broke out, which was increased by the two guardsmen, who took sides with one of the loungers, and by the scissors-grinder, who was equally hot upon the other side. A blow was struck, and in an instant the lady, who had stepped from her carriage, was the centre of a little knot of flushed and struggling men, who struck savagely at each other with their fists and sticks. Holmes dashed into the crowd to protect the lady; but just as he reached her he gave a cry and dropped to the ground, with the blood running freely down his face. At his fall the guardsmen took to their heels in one direction and the loungers in the other, while a number of better dressed people, who had watched the scuffle without taking part in it, crowded in to help the lady and to attend to the injured man. Irene Adler, as I will still call her, had hurried up the steps; but she stood at the top with her superb figure outlined against the lights of the hall, looking back into the street.

"Is the poor gentleman much hurt?" she asked.

"He is dead," cried several voices.

"No, no, there's life in him!" shouted another. "But he'll be gone before you can get him to hospital."

"He's a brave fellow," said a woman. "They would have had the lady's purse and watch if it hadn't been for him. They were a gang, and a rough one, too. Ah, he's breathing now."

"He can't lie in the street. May we bring him in, marm?"

"Surely. Bring him into the sitting-room. There is a comfortable sofa. This way, please!"

Slowly and solemnly he was borne into Briony Lodge and laid out in the principal room, while I still observed the proceedings from my post by the window. The lamps had been lit, but the blinds had not been drawn, so that I could see Holmes as he lay upon the couch. I do not know whether he was seized with compunction at that moment for the part he was playing, but I know that I never felt more heartily ashamed of myself in my life than when I saw the beautiful creature against whom I was conspiring, or the grace and kindliness with which she waited upon the injured man. And yet it would be the blackest treachery to Holmes to draw back now from the part which he had intrusted to me. I hardened my heart, and took the smoke-rocket from under my ulster. After all, I thought, we are not injuring her. We are but preventing her from injuring another.

Holmes had sat up upon the couch, and I saw him motion like a man who is in need of air. A maid rushed across and threw open the window. At the same instant I saw him raise his hand, and at the signal I tossed my rocket into the room with a cry of "Fire!" The word was no sooner out of my mouth than the whole crowd of spectators, well dressed and ill—gentlemen, ostlers, and servant-maids—joined in a general shriek of "Fire!" Thick clouds of smoke curled through the room and out at the open window. I caught a glimpse of rushing figures, and a moment later the voice of Holmes from within assuring them that it was a false alarm. Slipping through the shouting crowd I made my way to the corner of the street, and in ten minutes was rejoiced to find my friend's arm in mine, and to get away from the scene of uproar. He walked swiftly and in silence for some few minutes, until we had turned down one of the quiet streets which lead towards the Edgware Road.

"You did it very nicely, doctor," he remarked. "Nothing could have been better. It is all right."

"You have the photograph?"

"I know where it is."

"And how did you find out?"

"She showed me, as I told you that she would."

"I am still in the dark."

"I do not wish to make a mystery," said he, laughing. "The matter was perfectly simple. You, of course, saw that every one in the street was an accomplice. They were all engaged for the evening."

"I guessed as much."

"Then, when the row broke out, I had a little moist red paint in the palm of my hand. I rushed forward, fell down, clapped my hand to my face, and became a piteous spectacle. It is an old trick."

"That also I could fathom."

"Then they carried me in. She was bound to have me in. What else could she do? And into her sitting-room, which was the very room which I suspected. It lay between that and her bedroom, and I was determined to see which. They laid me on a couch, I motioned for air, they were compelled to open the window, and you had your chance."

"How did that help you?"

"It was all-important. When a woman thinks that her house is on fire, her instinct is at once to rush to the thing which she values most. It is a perfectly overpowering impulse, and I have more than once taken advantage of it. In the case of the Darlington Substitution Scandal it was of use to me, and also in the Arnsworth Castle business. A married woman grabs at her baby; an unmarried one reaches for her jewel-box. Now it was clear to me that our lady of to-day had nothing in the house more precious to her than what we are in quest of. She would rush to secure it. The alarm of fire was admirably done. The smoke and shouting were enough to shake nerves of steel. She responded beautifully. The photograph is in a recess behind a sliding panel just above the right bell-pull. She was there in an instant, and I caught a glimpse of it as she half-drew it out. When I cried out that it was a false alarm, she replaced it, glanced at the rocket, rushed from the room, and I have not seen her since. I rose, and, making my excuses, escaped from the house. I hesitated whether to attempt to secure the photograph at once; but the coachman had come in, and as he was watching me narrowly, it seemed safer to wait. A little over-precipitance may ruin all."

"And now?" I asked.

"Our quest is practically finished. I shall call with the King to-morrow, and with you, if you care to come with us. We will be shown into the sitting-room to wait for the lady, but it is probable that when she comes she may find neither us nor the photograph. It might be a satisfaction to His Majesty to regain it with his own hands."

"And when will you call?"

"At eight in the morning. She will not be up, so that we shall have a clear field. Besides, we must be prompt, for this marriage may mean a complete change in her life and habits. I must wire to the King without delay."

We had reached Baker Street, and had stopped at the door. He was searching his pockets for the key, when some one passing said:

"Good-night, Mister Sherlock Holmes."

There were several people on the pavement at the time, but the greeting appeared to come from a slim youth in an ulster who had hurried by.

"I've heard that voice before," said Holmes, staring down the dimly-lit street. "Now, I wonder who the deuce that could have been."

III

I slept at Baker Street that night, and we were engaged upon our toast and coffee in the morning when the King of Bohemia rushed into the room.

"You have really got it!" he cried, grasping Sherlock Holmes by either shoulder, and looking eagerly into his face.

"Not yet."

"But you have hopes?"

"I have hopes."

"Then, come. I am all impatience to be gone."

"We must have a cab."

"No, my brougham is waiting."

"Then that will simplify matters." We descended, and started off once more for Briony Lodge.

"Irene Adler is married," remarked Holmes.

"Married! When?"

"Yesterday."

"But to whom?"

"To an English lawyer named Norton."

"But she could not love him?"

"I am in hopes that she does."

"And why in hopes?"

"Because it would spare your Majesty all fear of future annoyance. If the lady loves her husband, she does not love your Majesty. If she does not love your Majesty, there is no reason why she should interfere with your Majesty's plan."

"It is true. And yet—Well! I wish she had been of my own station! What a queen she would have made!" He relapsed into a moody silence, which was not broken until we drew up in Serpentine Avenue.

The door of Briony Lodge was open, and an elderly woman stood upon the steps. She watched us with a sardonic eye as we stepped from the brougham.

"Mr. Sherlock Holmes, I believe?" said she.

"I am Mr. Holmes," answered my companion, looking at her with a questioning and rather startled gaze.

"Indeed! My mistress told me that you were likely to call. She left this morning with her husband by the 5.15 train from Charing Cross for the Continent."

"What!" Sherlock Holmes staggered back, white with chagrin and surprise. "Do you mean that she has left England?"

"Never to return."

"And the papers?" asked the King, hoarsely. "All is lost."

"We shall see." He pushed past the servant and rushed into the drawing-room, followed by the King and myself. The furniture was scattered about in every direction, with dismantled shelves and open drawers, as if the lady had hurriedly ransacked them before her flight. Holmes rushed at the bell-pull, tore back a small sliding shutter, and, plunging in his hand, pulled out a photograph and a letter. The photograph was of Irene Adler herself in evening dress, the letter was superscribed to "Sherlock Holmes, Esq. To be left till called for." My friend tore it open, and we all three read it together. It was dated at midnight of the preceding night, and ran in this way:

"My Dear Mr. Sherlock Holmes,—You really did it very well. You took me in completely. Until after the alarm of fire, I had not a suspicion. But then, when I found how I had betrayed myself, I began to think. I had been warned against you months ago. I had been told that, if the King employed an agent, it would certainly be you. And your address had been given me. Yet, with all this, you made me reveal what you wanted to know. Even after I became suspicious, I found it hard to think evil of such a dear, kind old clergyman. But, you know, I have been trained as an actress myself. Male costume is nothing new to me. I often take advantage of the freedom which it gives. I sent John, the coachman, to watch you, ran up-stairs, got into my walking-clothes, as I call them, and came down just as you departed.

"Well, I followed you to your door, and so made sure that I was really an object of interest to the celebrated Mr. Sherlock Holmes. Then I, rather imprudently, wished you good-night, and started for the Temple to see my husband.

"We both thought the best resource was flight, when pursued by so formidable an antagonist; so you will find the nest empty when you call to-morrow. As to the photograph, your client may rest in peace. I love and am loved by a better man than he. The King may do what he will without hinderance from one whom he has cruelly wronged. I keep it only to safeguard myself, and to preserve a weapon which will always secure me from any steps which he might take in the future. I leave a photograph which   he might care to possess; and I remain, dear Mr. Sherlock Holmes, very truly yours,

Irene Norton, née Adler."

"What a woman—oh, what a woman!" cried the King of Bohemia, when we had all three read this epistle. "Did I not tell you how quick and resolute she was? Would she not have made an admirable queen? Is it not a pity that she was not on my level?"

"From what I have seen of the lady she seems indeed to be on a very different level to your Majesty," said Holmes, coldly. "I am sorry that I have not been able to bring your Majesty's business to a more successful conclusion."

"On the contrary, my dear sir," cried the King; "nothing could be more successful. I know that her word is inviolate. The photograph is now as safe as if it were in the fire."

"I am glad to hear your Majesty say so."

"I am immensely indebted to you. Pray tell me in what way I can reward you. This ring—" He slipped an emerald snake ring from his finger and held it out upon the palm of his hand.

"Your Majesty has something which I should value even more highly," said Holmes.

"You have but to name it."

"This photograph!"

The King stared at him in amazement.

"Irene's photograph!" he cried. "Certainly, if you wish it."

"I thank your Majesty. Then there is no more to be done in the matter. I have the honor to wish you a very good-morning." He bowed, and, turning away without observing the hand which the King had stretched out to him, he set off in my company for his chambers.

And that was how a great scandal threatened to affect the kingdom of Bohemia, and how the best plans of Mr. Sherlock Holmes were beaten by a woman's wit. He used to make merry over the cleverness of women, but I have not heard him do it of late. And when he speaks of Irene Adler, or when he refers to her photograph, it is always under the honorable title of the woman.

THE ADVENTURE OF THE SPECKLED BAND (1892)

SIR ARTHUR CONAN DOYLE (1859-1930)

On glancing over my notes of the seventy odd cases in which I have during the last eight years studied the methods of my friend Sherlock Holmes, I find many tragic, some comic, a large number merely strange, but none commonplace; for, working as he did rather for the love of his art than for the acquirement of wealth, he refused to associate himself with any investigation which did not tend towards the unusual, and even the fantastic. Of all these varied cases, however, I cannot recall any which presented more singular features than that which was associated with the well-known Surrey family of the Roylotts of Stoke Moran. The events in question occurred in the early days of my association with Holmes, when we were sharing rooms as bachelors in Baker Street. It is possible that I might have placed them upon record before, but a promise of secrecy was made at the time, from which I have only been freed during the last month by the untimely death of the lady to whom the pledge was given. It is perhaps as well that the facts should now come to light, for I have reasons to know that there are wide-spread rumors as to the death of Dr. Grimesby Roylott which tend to make the matter even more terrible than the truth.

It was early in April in the year '83 that I woke one morning to find Sherlock Holmes standing, fully dressed, by the side of my bed. He was a late riser as a rule, and as the clock on the mantel-piece showed me that it was only a quarter past seven, I blinked up at him in some surprise, and perhaps just a little resentment, for I was myself regular in my habits.

"Very sorry to knock you up, Watson," said he, "but it's the common lot this morning. Mrs. Hudson has been knocked up, she retorted upon me, and I on you."

"What is it, then—a fire?"

"No; a client. It seems that a young lady has arrived in a considerable state of excitement, who insists upon seeing me. She is waiting now in the sitting-room. Now, when young ladies wander about the metropolis at this hour of the morning, and knock sleepy people up out of their beds, I presume that it is something very pressing which they have to communicate. Should it prove to be an interesting case, you would, I am sure, wish to follow it from the outset. I thought, at any rate, that I should call you and give you the chance."

"My dear fellow, I would not miss it for anything."

I had no keener pleasure than in following Holmes in his professional investigations, and in admiring the rapid deductions, as swift as intuitions, and yet always founded on a logical basis, with which he unravelled the problems which were submitted to him. I rapidly threw on my clothes, and was ready in a few minutes to accompany my friend down to the sitting-room. A lady dressed in black and heavily veiled, who had been sitting in the window, rose as we entered.

"Good-morning, madam," said Holmes, cheerily. "My name is Sherlock Holmes. This is my intimate friend and associate, Dr. Watson, before whom you can speak as freely as before myself. Ha! I am glad to see that Mrs. Hudson has had the good sense to light the fire. Pray draw up to it, and I shall order you a cup of hot coffee, for I observe that you are shivering."

"It is not cold which makes me shiver," said the woman, in a low voice, changing her seat as requested.

"What, then?"

"It is fear, Mr. Holmes. It is terror." She raised her veil as she spoke, and we could see that she was indeed in a pitiable state of agitation, her face all drawn and gray, with restless, frightened eyes, like those of some hunted animal. Her features and figure were those of a woman of thirty, but her hair was shot with premature gray, and her expression was weary and haggard. Sherlock Holmes ran her over with one of his quick, all-comprehensive glances.

"You must not fear," said he, soothingly, bending forward and patting her forearm. "We shall soon set matters right, I have no doubt. You have come in by train this morning, I see."

"You know me, then?"

"No, but I observe the second half of a return ticket in the palm of your left glove. You must have started early, and yet you had a good drive in a dog-cart, along heavy roads, before you reached the station."

The lady gave a violent start, and stared in bewilderment at my companion.

"There is no mystery, my dear madam," said he, smiling. "The left arm of your jacket is spattered with mud in no less than seven places. The marks are perfectly fresh. There is no vehicle save a dog-cart which throws up mud in that way, and then only when you sit on the left-hand side of the driver."

"Whatever your reasons may be, you are perfectly correct," said she. "I started from home before six, reached Leatherhead at twenty past, and came in by the first train to Waterloo. Sir, I can stand this strain no longer;

I shall go mad if it continues. I have no one to turn to—none, save only one, who cares for me, and he, poor fellow, can be of little aid. I have heard of you, Mr. Holmes; I have heard of you from Mrs. Farintosh, whom you helped in the hour of her sore need. It was from her that I had your address. Oh, sir, do you not think that you could help me, too, and at least throw a little light through the dense darkness which surrounds me? At present it is out of my power to reward you for your services, but in a month or six weeks I shall be married, with the control of my own income, and then at least you shall not find me ungrateful."

Holmes turned to his desk, and unlocking it, drew out a small case-book, which he consulted.

"Farintosh," said he. "Ah yes, I recall the case; it was concerned with an opal tiara. I think it was before your time, Watson. I can only say, madam, that I shall be happy to devote the same care to your case as I did to that of your friend. As to reward, my profession is its own reward; but you are at liberty to defray whatever expenses I may be put to, at the time which suits you best. And now I beg that you will lay before us everything that may help us in forming an opinion upon the matter."

"Alas!" replied our visitor, "the very horror of my situation lies in the fact that my fears are so vague, and my suspicions depend so entirely upon small points, which might seem trivial to another, that even he to whom of all others I have a right to look for help and advice looks upon all that I tell him about it as the fancies of a nervous woman. He does not say so, but I can read it from his soothing answers and averted eyes. But I have heard, Mr. Holmes, that you can see deeply into the manifold wickedness of the human heart. You may advise me how to walk amid the dangers which encompass me."

"I am all attention, madam."

"My name is Helen Stoner, and I am living with my step-father, who is the last survivor of one of the oldest Saxon families in England, the Roylotts of Stoke Moran, on the western border of Surrey."

Holmes nodded his head. "The name is familiar to me," said he.

"The family was at one time among the richest in England, and the estates extended over the borders into Berkshire in the north, and Hampshire in the west. In the last century, however, four successive heirs were of a dissolute and wasteful disposition, and the family ruin was eventually completed by a gambler in the days of the Regency. Nothing was left save a few acres of ground, and the two-hundred-year-old house, which is itself crushed under a heavy mortgage. The last squire dragged out his existence there, living the horrible life of an aristocratic pauper; but his only son, my step-father, seeing that he must adapt himself to the new conditions, obtained an advance from a relative, which enabled him to take a medical degree, and went out to Calcutta, where, by his professional skill and his force of character, he established a large practice. In a fit of anger, however, caused by some robberies which had been perpetrated in the house, he beat his native butler to death, and narrowly escaped a capital sentence. As it was, he suffered a long term of imprisonment, and afterwards returned to England a morose and disappointed man.

"When Dr. Roylott was in India he married my mother, Mrs. Stoner, the young widow of Major-general Stoner, of the Bengal Artillery. My sister Julia and I were twins, and we were only two years old at the time of my mother's re-marriage. She had a considerable sum of money—not less than £1000 a year—and this she bequeathed to Dr. Roylott entirely while we resided with him, with a provision that a certain annual sum should be allowed to each of us in the event of our marriage. Shortly after our return to England my mother died—she was killed eight years ago in a railway accident near Crewe. Dr. Roylott then abandoned his attempts to establish himself in practice in London, and took us to live with him in the old ancestral house at Stoke Moran. The money which my mother had left was enough for all our wants, and there seemed to be no obstacle to our happiness.

"But a terrible change came over our step-father about this time. Instead of making friends and exchanging visits with our neighbors, who had at first been overjoyed to see a Roylott of Stoke Moran back in the old family seat, he shut himself up in his house, and seldom came out save to indulge in ferocious quarrels with whoever might cross his path. Violence of temper approaching to mania has been hereditary in the men of the family, and in my step-father's case it had, I believe, been intensified by his long residence in the tropics. A series of disgraceful brawls took place, two of which ended in the police-court, until at last he became the terror of the village, and the folks would fly at his approach, for he is a man of immense strength, and absolutely uncontrollable in his anger.

"Last week he hurled the local blacksmith over a parapet into a stream, and it was only by paying over all the money which I could gather together that I was able to avert another public exposure. He had no friends at all save the wandering gypsies, and he would give these vagabonds leave to encamp upon the few acres of bramble-covered land which represent the family estate, and would accept in return the hospitality of their tents, wandering away with them sometimes for weeks on end. He has a passion also for Indian animals, which are sent over to him by a correspondent, and he has at this moment a cheetah and a baboon, which wander freely over his grounds, and are feared by the villagers almost as much as their master.

"You can imagine from what I say that my poor sister Julia and I had no great pleasure in our lives. No servant would stay with us, and for a long time we did all the work of the house. She was but thirty at the time of her death, and yet her hair had already begun to whiten, even as mine has."

"Your sister is dead, then?"

"She died just two years ago, and it is of her death that I wish to speak to you. You can understand that, living the life which I have described, we were little likely to see anyone of our own age and position. We had, however, an aunt, my mother's maiden sister, Miss Honoria Westphail, who lives near Harrow, and we were occasionally allowed to pay short visits at this lady's house. Julia went there at Christmas two years ago, and met there a half-pay major of marines, to whom she became engaged. My step-father learned of the engagement when my sister returned, and offered no objection to the marriage; but within a fortnight of the day which had been fixed for the wedding, the terrible event occurred which has deprived me of my only companion."

Sherlock Holmes had been leaning back in his chair with his eyes closed and his head sunk in a cushion, but he half opened his lids now and glanced across at his visitor.

"Pray be precise as to details," said he.

"It is easy for me to be so, for every event of that dreadful time is seared into my memory. The manor-house is, as I have already said, very old, and only one wing is now inhabited. The bedrooms in this wing are on the ground floor, the sitting-rooms being in the central block of the buildings. Of these bedrooms the first is Dr. Roylott's, the second my sister's, and the third my own. There is no communication between them, but they all open out into the same corridor. Do I make myself plain?"

"Perfectly so."

"The windows of the three rooms open out upon the lawn. That fatal night Dr. Roylott had gone to his room early, though we knew that he had not retired to rest, for my sister was troubled by the smell of the strong Indian cigars which it was his custom to smoke. She left her room, therefore, and came into mine, where she sat for some time, chatting about her approaching wedding. At eleven o'clock she rose to leave me but she paused at the door and looked back.

"'Tell me, Helen,' said she, 'have you ever heard any one whistle in the dead of the night?'

"'Never,' said I.

"'I suppose that you could not possibly whistle, yourself, in your sleep?'

"'Certainly not. But why?'

"'Because during the last few nights I have always, about three in the morning, heard a low, clear whistle. I am a light sleeper, and it has awakened me. I cannot tell where it came from—perhaps from the next room, perhaps from the lawn. I thought that I would just ask you whether you had heard it.'

"'No, I have not. It must be those wretched gypsies in the plantation.'

"'Very likely. And yet if it were on the lawn, I wonder that you did not hear it also.'

"'Ah, but I sleep more heavily than you.'

"'Well, it is of no great consequence, at any rate.' She smiled back at me, closed my door, and a few moments later I heard her key turn in the lock."

"Indeed," said Holmes. "Was it your custom always to lock yourselves in at night?"

"Always."

"And why?"

"I think that I mentioned to you that the doctor kept a cheetah and a baboon. We had no feeling of security unless our doors were locked."

"Quite so. Pray proceed with your statement."

"I could not sleep that night. A vague feeling of impending misfortune impressed me. My sister and I, you will recollect, were twins, and you know how subtle are the links which bind two souls which are so closely allied. It was a wild night. The wind was howling outside, and the rain was beating and splashing against the windows. Suddenly, amid all the hubbub of the gale, there burst forth the wild scream of a terrified woman. I knew that it was my sister's voice. I sprang from my bed, wrapped a shawl round me, and rushed into the corridor. As I opened my door I seemed to hear a low whistle, such as my sister described, and a few moments later a clanging sound, as if a mass of metal had fallen. As I ran down the passage, my sister's door was unlocked, and revolved slowly upon its hinges. I stared at it horror-stricken, not knowing what was about to issue from it. By the light of the corridor-lamp I saw my sister appear at the opening, her face blanched with terror, her hands groping for help, her whole figure swaying to and fro like that of a drunkard. I ran to her and threw my arms round her, but at that moment her knees seemed to give way and she fell to the ground. She writhed as one who is in terrible pain, and her limbs were dreadfully convulsed. At first I thought that she had not recognized me, but as I bent over her she suddenly shrieked out in a voice which I shall never forget, 'Oh, my God! Helen! It was the band! The speckled band!' There was something else which she would fain have said, and she stabbed with her finger into the air in the direction of the doctor's room, but a fresh convulsion seized her and choked her words. I rushed out, calling loudly for my step-father, and I met him hastening from his room in his dressing-gown. When he reached my sister's side she was unconscious, and though he poured brandy down her throat and sent for medical aid from the village, all efforts were in vain, for she slowly sank and died without having recovered her consciousness. Such was the dreadful end of my beloved sister."

"One moment," said Holmes; "are you sure about this whistle and metallic sound? Could you swear to it?"

"That was what the county coroner asked me at the inquiry. It is my strong impression that I heard it, and yet, among the crash of the gale and the creaking of an old house, I may possibly have been deceived."

"Was your sister dressed?"

"No, she was in her night-dress. In her right hand was found the charred stump of a match, and in her left a matchbox."

"Showing that she had struck a light and looked about her when the alarm took place. That is important. And what conclusions did the coroner come to?"

"He investigated the case with great care, for Dr. Roylott's conduct had long been notorious in the county, but he was unable to find any satisfactory cause of death. My evidence showed that the door had been fastened upon the inner side, and the windows were blocked by old-fashioned shutters with broad iron bars, which were secured every night. The walls were carefully sounded, and were shown to be quite solid all round, and the flooring was also thoroughly examined, with the same result. The chimney is wide, but is barred up by four large staples. It is certain, therefore, that my sister was quite alone when she met her end. Besides, there were no marks of any violence upon her."

"How about poison?"

"The doctors examined her for it, but without success."

"What do you think that this unfortunate lady died of, then?"

"It is my belief that she died of pure fear and nervous shock, though what it was that frightened her I cannot imagine."

"Were there gypsies in the plantation at the time?"

"Yes, there are nearly always some there."

"Ah, and what did you gather from this allusion to a band—a speckled band?"

"Sometimes I have thought that it was merely the wild talk of delirium, sometimes that it may have referred to some band of people, perhaps to these very gypsies in the plantation. I do not know whether the spotted handkerchiefs which so many of them wear over their heads might have suggested the strange adjective which she used."

Holmes shook his head like a man who is far from being satisfied.

"These are very deep waters," said he; "pray go on with your narrative."

"Two years have passed since then, and my life has been until lately lonelier than ever. A month ago, however, a dear friend, whom I have known for many years, has done me the honor to ask my hand in marriage. His name is Armitage—Percy Armitage—the second son of Mr. Armitage, of Crane Water, near Reading. My step-father has offered no opposition to the match, and we are to be married in the course of the spring. Two days ago some repairs were started in the west wing of the building, and my bedroom wall has been pierced, so that I have had to move into the chamber in which my sister died, and to sleep in the very bed in which she slept. Imagine, then, my thrill of terror when last night, as I lay awake, thinking over her terrible fate, I suddenly heard in the silence of the night the low whistle which had been the herald of her own death. I sprang up and lit the lamp, but nothing was to be seen in the room. I was too shaken to go to bed again, however, so I dressed, and as soon as it was daylight I slipped down, got a dog-cart at the 'Crown Inn,' which is opposite, and drove to Leatherhead, from whence I have come on this morning with the one object of seeing you and asking your advice."

"You have done wisely," said my friend. "But have you told me all?"
"Yes, all."
"Miss Roylott, you have not. You are screening your step-father."
"Why, what do you mean?"
For answer Holmes pushed back the frill of black lace which fringed the hand that lay upon our visitor's knee. Five little livid spots, the marks of four fingers and a thumb, were printed upon the white wrist.
"You have been cruelly used," said Holmes.
The lady colored deeply and covered over her injured wrist. "He is a hard man," she said, "and perhaps he hardly knows his own strength."
There was a long silence, during which Holmes leaned his chin upon his hands and stared into the crackling fire.
"This is a very deep business," he said, at last. "There are a thousand details which I should desire to know before I decide upon our course of action. Yet we have not a moment to lose. If we were to come to Stoke Moran to-day, would it be possible for us to see over these rooms without the knowledge of your step-father?"
"As it happens, he spoke of coming into town to-day upon some most important business. It is probable that he will be away all day, and that there would be nothing to disturb you. We have a house-keeper now, but she is old and foolish, and I could easily get her out of the way."
"Excellent. You are not averse to this trip, Watson?"
"By no means."
"Then we shall both come. What are you going to do yourself?"
"I have one or two things which I would wish to do now that I am in

town. But I shall return by the twelve o'clock train, so as to be there in time for your coming."

"And you may expect us early in the afternoon. I have myself some small business matters to attend to. Will you not wait and breakfast?"

"No, I must go. My heart is lightened already since I have confided my trouble to you. I shall look forward to seeing you again this afternoon." She dropped her thick black veil over her face and glided from the room.

"And what do you think of it all, Watson?" asked Sherlock Holmes, leaning back in his chair.

"It seems to me to be a most dark and sinister business."

"Dark enough and sinister enough."

"Yet if the lady is correct in saying that the flooring and walls are sound, and that the door, window, and chimney are impassable, then her sister must have been undoubtedly alone when she met her mysterious end."

"What becomes, then, of these nocturnal whistles, and what of the very peculiar words of the dying woman?"

"I cannot think."

"When you combine the ideas of whistles at night, the presence of a band of gypsies who are on intimate terms with this old doctor, the fact that we have every reason to believe that the doctor has an interest in preventing his step-daughter's marriage, the dying allusion to a band, and, finally, the fact that Miss Helen Stoner heard a metallic clang, which might have been caused by one of those metal bars which secured the shutters falling back into their place, I think that there is good ground to think that the mystery may be cleared along those lines."

"But what, then, did the gypsies do?"

"I cannot imagine."

"I see many objections to any such theory."

"And so do I. It is precisely for that reason that we are going to Stoke Moran this day. I want to see whether the objections are fatal, or if they may be explained away. But what in the name of the devil!"

The ejaculation had been drawn from my companion by the fact that our door had been suddenly dashed open, and that a huge man had framed himself in the aperture. His costume was a peculiar mixture of the professional and of the agricultural, having a black top-hat, a long frock-coat, and a pair of high gaiters, with a hunting-crop swinging in his hand. So tall was he that his hat actually brushed the cross bar of the doorway, and his breadth seemed to span it across from side to side. A large face, seared with a thousand wrinkles, burned yellow with the sun, and marked with every evil passion, was turned from one to the other of us, while his deep-set, bile-shot eyes, and his high, thin, fleshless nose, gave him somewhat the resemblance to a fierce old bird of prey.

"Which of you is Holmes?" asked this apparition.

"My name, sir; but you have the advantage of me," said my companion, quietly.

"I am Dr. Grimesby Roylott, of Stoke Moran."

"Indeed, doctor," said Holmes, blandly. "Pray take a seat."

"I will do nothing of the kind. My step-daughter has been here. I have traced her. What has she been saying to you?"

"It is a little cold for the time of the year," said Holmes.

"What has she been saying to you?" screamed the old man, furiously.

"But I have heard that the crocuses promise well," continued my companion, imperturbably.

"Ha! You put me off, do you?" said our new visitor, taking a step forward and shaking his hunting-crop. "I know you, you scoundrel! I have heard of you before. You are Holmes, the meddler."

My friend smiled.

"Holmes, the busybody!"

His smile broadened.

"Holmes, the Scotland-yard Jack-in-office!"

Holmes chuckled heartily. "Your conversation is most entertaining," said he. "When you go out close the door, for there is a decided draught."

"I will go when I have said my say. Don't you dare to meddle with my affairs. I know that Miss Stoner has been here. I traced her! I am a dangerous man to fall foul of! See here." He stepped swiftly forward, seized the poker, and bent it into a curve with his huge brown hands.

"See that you keep yourself out of my grip," he snarled, and hurling the twisted poker into the fireplace, he strode out of the room.

"He seems a very amiable person," said Holmes, laughing. "I am not quite so bulky, but if he had remained I might have shown him that my grip was not much more feeble than his own." As he spoke he picked up the steel poker, and with a sudden effort straightened it out again.

"Fancy his having the insolence to confound me with the official detective force! This incident gives zest to our investigation, however, and I only trust that our little friend will not suffer from her imprudence in allowing this brute to trace her. And now, Watson, we shall order breakfast, and afterwards I shall walk down to Doctors' Commons, where I hope to get some data which may help us in this matter."

It was nearly one o'clock when Sherlock Holmes returned from his excursion. He held in his hand a sheet of blue paper, scrawled over with notes and figures.

"I have seen the will of the deceased wife," said he. "To determine its exact meaning I have been obliged to work out the present prices of the investments with which it is concerned. The total income, which at the time of the wife's death was little short of £1100, is now, through the fall in agricultural prices, not more than £750. Each daughter can claim an income of £250, in case of marriage. It is evident, therefore, that if both girls had married, this beauty would have had a mere pittance, while even one of them would cripple him to a very serious extent. My morning's work has not been wasted, since it has proved that he has the very strongest motives for standing in the way of anything of the sort. And now, Watson, this is too serious for dawdling, especially as the old man is aware that we are interesting ourselves in his affairs; so if you are ready, we shall call a cab and drive to Waterloo. I should be very much obliged if you would slip your revolver into your pocket. An Eley's No. 2 is an excellent argument with gentlemen who can twist steel pokers into knots. That and a toothbrush are, I think, all that we need."

At Waterloo we were fortunate in catching a train for Leatherhead, where we hired a trap at the station inn, and drove for four or five miles through the lovely Surrey lanes. It was a perfect day, with a bright sun and a few fleecy clouds in the heavens. The trees and way-side hedges were just throwing out their first green shoots, and the air was full of the pleasant smell of the moist earth. To me at least there was a strange contrast between the sweet promise of the spring and this sinister quest upon which we were engaged. My companion sat in the front of the trap, his arms folded, his hat pulled down over his eyes, and his chin sunk upon his breast, buried in the deepest thought. Suddenly, however, he started, tapped me on the shoulder, and pointed over the meadows.

"Look there!" said he.

A heavily-timbered park stretched up in a gentle slope, thickening into a grove at the highest point. From amid the branches there jutted out the gray gables and high roof-tree of a very old mansion.

"Stoke Moran?" said he.

"Yes, sir, that be the house of Dr. Grimesby Roylott," remarked the driver.

"There is some building going on there," said Holmes; "that is where we are going."

"There's the village," said the driver, pointing to a cluster of roofs some distance to the left; "but if you want to get to the house, you'll find it shorter to get over this stile, and so by the foot-path over the fields. There it is, where the lady is walking."

"And the lady, I fancy, is Miss Stoner," observed Holmes, shading his eyes. "Yes, I think we had better do as you suggest."

We got off, paid our fare, and the trap rattled back on its way to Leatherhead.

"I thought it as well," said Holmes, as we climbed the stile, "that this fellow should think we had come here as architects, or on some definite business. It may stop his gossip. Good-afternoon, Miss Stoner. You see that we have been as good as our word."

Our client of the morning had hurried forward to meet us with a face which spoke her joy. "I have been waiting so eagerly for you," she cried, shaking hands with us warmly. "All has turned out splendidly. Dr. Roylott has gone to town, and it is unlikely that he will be back before evening."

"We have had the pleasure of making the doctor's acquaintance," said Holmes, and in a few words he sketched out what had occurred. Miss Stoner turned white to the lips as she listened.

"Good heavens!" she cried, "he has followed me, then."

"So it appears."

"He is so cunning that I never know when I am safe from him. What will he say when he returns?"

"He must guard himself, for he may find that there is some one more cunning than himself upon his track. You must lock yourself up from him to-night. If he is violent, we shall take you away to your aunt's at Harrow. Now, we must make the best use of our time, so kindly take us at once to the rooms which we are to examine."

The building was of gray, lichen-blotched stone, with a high central portion, and two curving wings, like the claws of a crab, thrown out on each side. In one of these wings the windows were broken, and blocked with wooden boards, while the roof was partly caved in, a picture of ruin. The central portion was in little better repair, but the right-hand block was comparatively modern, and the blinds in the windows, with the blue smoke curling up from the chimneys, showed that this was where the family resided. Some scaffolding had been erected against the end wall, and the stone-work had been broken into, but there were no signs of any workmen at the moment of our visit. Holmes walked slowly up and down the ill-trimmed lawn, and examined with deep attention the outsides of the windows.

"This, I take it, belongs to the room in which you used to sleep, the centre one to your sister's, and the one next to the main building to Dr. Roylott's chamber?"

"Exactly so. But I am now sleeping in the middle one."

"Pending the alterations, as I understand. By-the-way, there does not seem to be any very pressing need for repairs at that end wall."

"There were none. I believe that it was an excuse to move me from my room."

"Ah! That is suggestive. Now, on the other side of this narrow wing runs the corridor from which these three rooms open. There are windows in it, of course?"

"Yes, but very small ones. Too narrow for any one to pass through."

"As you both locked your doors at night, your rooms were unapproachable from that side. Now, would you have the kindness to go into your room and bar your shutters."

Miss Stoner did so, and Holmes, after a careful examination through the open window, endeavored in every way to force the shutter open, but without success. There was no slit through which a knife could be passed to raise the bar. Then with his lens he tested the hinges, but they were of solid iron, built firmly into the massive masonry. "Hum!" said he, scratching his chin in some perplexity; "my theory certainly presents some difficulties. No one could pass these shutters if they were bolted. Well, we shall see if the inside throws any light upon the matter."

A small side door led into the whitewashed corridor from which the three bedrooms opened. Holmes refused to examine the third chamber, so we passed at once to the second, that in which Miss Stoner was now sleeping, and in which her sister had met with her fate. It was a homely little room, with a low ceiling and a gaping fireplace, after the fashion of old country-houses. A brown chest of drawers stood in one corner, a narrow white-counterpaned bed in another, and a dressing-table on the left-hand side of the window. These articles, with two small wicker-work chairs, made up all the furniture in the room, save for a square of Wilton carpet in the centre. The boards round and the panelling of the walls were of brown, worm-eaten oak, so old and discolored that it may have dated from the original building of the house. Holmes drew one of the chairs into a corner and sat silent, while his eyes travelled round and round and up and down, taking in every detail of the apartment.

"Where does that bell communicate with?" he asked, at last, pointing to a thick bell-rope which hung down beside the bed, the tassel actually lying upon the pillow.

"It goes to the house-keeper's room."

"It looks newer than the other things?"

"Yes, it was only put there a couple of years ago."

"Your sister asked for it, I suppose?"

"No, I never heard of her using it. We used always to get what we wanted for ourselves."

"Indeed, it seemed unnecessary to put so nice a bell-pull there. You will excuse me for a few minutes while I satisfy myself as to this floor." He threw himself down upon his face with his lens in his hand, and crawled swiftly backward and forward, examining minutely the cracks between the boards. Then he did the same with the wood-work with which the chamber was panelled. Finally he walked over to the bed, and spent some time in staring at it, and in running his eye up and down the wall. Finally he took the bell-rope in his hand and gave it a brisk tug.

"Why, it's a dummy," said he.

"Won't it ring?"

"No, it is not even attached to a wire. This is very interesting. You can see now that it is fastened to a hook just above where the little opening for the ventilator is."

"How very absurd! I never noticed that before."

"Very strange!" muttered Holmes, pulling at the rope. "There are one or two very singular points about this room. For example, what a fool a builder must be to open a ventilator into another room, when, with the same trouble, he might have communicated with the outside air!"

"That is also quite modern," said the lady.

"Done about the same time as the bell-rope?" remarked Holmes.

"Yes, there were several little changes carried out about that time."

"They seem to have been of a most interesting character—dummy bell-ropes, and ventilators which do not ventilate. With your permission, Miss Stoner, we shall now carry our researches into the inner apartment."

Dr. Grimesby Roylott's chamber was larger than that of his step-daughter, but was as plainly furnished. A camp-bed, a small wooden shelf full of books, mostly of a technical character, an arm-chair beside the bed, a plain wooden chair against the wall, a round table, and a large iron safe were the principal things which met the eye. Holmes walked slowly round and examined each and all of them with the keenest interest.

"What's in here?" he asked, tapping the safe.

"My step-father's business papers."

"Oh! You have seen inside, then?"

"Only once, some years ago. I remember that it was full of papers."

"There isn't a cat in it, for example?"

"No. What a strange idea!"

"Well, look at this!" He took up a small saucer of milk which stood on the top of it.

"No; we don't keep a cat. But there is a cheetah and a baboon."

"Ah, yes, of course! Well, a cheetah is just a big cat, and yet a saucer of milk does not go very far in satisfying its wants, I dare say. There is one point which I should wish to determine." He squatted down in front of the wooden chair, and examined the seat of it with the greatest attention.

"Thank you. That is quite settled," said he, rising and putting his lens in his pocket.

"Hello! Here is something interesting!"

The object which had caught his eye was a small dog-lash hung on one corner of the bed. The lash, however, was curled upon itself, and tied so as to make a loop of whip-cord.

"What do you make of that, Watson?"

"It's a common enough lash. But I don't know why it should be tied."

"That is not quite so common, is it? Ah, me! It's a wicked world, and when a clever man turns his brains to crime it is the worst of all. I think that I have seen enough now, Miss Stoner, and with your permission we shall walk out upon the lawn."

I had never seen my friend's face so grim or his brow so dark as it was when we turned from the scene of this investigation. We had walked several times up and down the lawn, neither Miss Stoner nor myself liking to break in upon his thoughts before he roused himself from his reverie.

"It is very essential, Miss Stoner," said he, "that you should absolutely follow my advice in every respect."

"I shall most certainly do so."

"The matter is too serious for any hesitation. Your life may depend upon your compliance."

"I assure you that I am in your hands."

"In the first place, both my friend and I must spend the night in your room."

Both Miss Stoner and I gazed at him in astonishment.

"Yes, it must be so. Let me explain. I believe that that is the village inn over there?"

"Yes, that is the 'Crown.'"

"Very good. Your windows would be visible from there?"

"Certainly."

"You must confine yourself to your room, on pretence of a headache, when your step-father comes back. Then when you hear him retire for the night, you must open the shutters of your window, undo the hasp, put your lamp there as a signal to us, and then withdraw quietly with everything which you are likely to want into the room which you used to occupy. I have no doubt that, in spite of the repairs, you could manage there for one night."

"Oh yes, easily."

"The rest you will leave in our hands."

"But what will you do?"

"We shall spend the night in your room, and we shall investigate the cause of this noise which has disturbed you."

"I believe, Mr. Holmes, that you have already made up your mind," said Miss Stoner, laying her hand upon my companion's sleeve.

"Perhaps I have."

"Then for pity's sake tell me what was the cause of my sister's death."

"I should prefer to have clearer proofs before I speak."

"You can at least tell me whether my own thought is correct, and if she died from some sudden fright."

"No, I do not think so. I think that there was probably some more tangible cause. And now, Miss Stoner, we must leave you, for if Dr. Roylott returned and saw us, our journey would be in vain. Good-bye, and be brave, for if you will do what I have told you, you may rest assured that we shall soon drive away the dangers that threaten you."

Sherlock Holmes and I had no difficulty in engaging a bedroom and sitting-room at the "Crown Inn." They were on the upper floor, and from our window we could command a view of the avenue gate, and of the inhabited wing of Stoke Moran Manor House. At dusk we saw Dr. Grimesby Roylott drive past, his huge form looming up beside the little figure of the lad who drove him. The boy had some slight difficulty in undoing the heavy iron gates, and we heard the hoarse roar of the doctor's voice, and saw the fury with which he shook his clinched fists at him. The trap drove on, and a few minutes later we saw a sudden light spring up among the trees as the lamp was lit in one of the sitting-rooms.

"Do you know, Watson," said Holmes, as we sat together in the gathering darkness, "I have really some scruples as to taking you to-night. There is a distinct element of danger."

"Can I be of assistance?"

"Your presence might be invaluable."

"Then I shall certainly come."

"It is very kind of you."

"You speak of danger. You have evidently seen more in these rooms than was visible to me."

"No, but I fancy that I may have deduced a little more. I imagine that you saw all that I did."

"I saw nothing remarkable save the bell-rope, and what purpose that could answer I confess is more than I can imagine."

"You saw the ventilator, too?"

"Yes, but I do not think that it is such a very unusual thing to have a small opening between two rooms. It was so small that a rat could hardly pass through."

"I knew that we should find a ventilator before ever we came to Stoke Moran."

"My dear Holmes!"

"Oh yes, I did. You remember in her statement she said that her sister could smell Dr. Roylott's cigar. Now, of course that suggested at once that there must be a communication between the two rooms. It could only be a small one, or it would have been remarked upon at the coroner's inquiry. I deduced a ventilator."

"But what harm can there be in that?"

"Well, there is at least a curious coincidence of dates. A ventilator is made, a cord is hung, and a lady who sleeps in the bed dies. Does not that strike you?"

"I cannot as yet see any connection."

"Did you observe anything very peculiar about that bed?"

"No."

"It was clamped to the floor. Did you ever see a bed fastened like that before?"

"I cannot say that I have."

"The lady could not move her bed. It must always be in the same relative position to the ventilator and to the rope—for so we may call it, since it was clearly never meant for a bell-pull."

"Holmes," I cried, "I seem to see dimly what you are hinting at. We are only just in time to prevent some subtle and horrible crime."

"Subtle enough and horrible enough. When a doctor does go wrong, he is the first of criminals. He has nerve and he has knowledge. Palmer and Pritchard were among the heads of their profession. This man strikes even deeper, but I think, Watson, that we shall be able to strike deeper still. But we shall have horrors enough before the night is over; for goodness' sake let us have a quiet pipe, and turn our minds for a few hours to something more cheerful."

About nine o'clock the light among the trees was extinguished, and all was dark in the direction of the Manor House. Two hours passed slowly away, and then, suddenly, just at the stroke of eleven, a single bright light shone out right in front of us.

"That is our signal," said Holmes, springing to his feet; "it comes from the middle window."

As we passed out he exchanged a few words with the landlord, explaining that we were going on a late visit to an acquaintance, and that it was possible that we might spend the night there. A moment later we were out on the dark road, a chill wind blowing in our faces, and one yellow light twinkling in front of us through the gloom to guide us on our sombre errand.

There was little difficulty in entering the grounds, for unrepaired breaches gaped in the old park wall. Making our way among the trees, we reached the lawn, crossed it, and were about to enter through the window, when out from a clump of laurel bushes there darted what seemed to be a hideous and distorted child, who threw itself upon the grass with writhing limbs, and then ran swiftly across the lawn into the darkness.

"My God!" I whispered; "did you see it?"

Holmes was for the moment as startled as I. His hand closed like a vice upon my wrist in his agitation. Then he broke into a low laugh, and put his lips to my ear.

"It is a nice household," he murmured. "That is the baboon."

I had forgotten the strange pets which the doctor affected. There was a cheetah, too; perhaps we might find it upon our shoulders at any moment. I confess that I felt easier in my mind when, after following Holmes's example and slipping off my shoes, I found myself inside the bedroom. My companion noiselessly closed the shutters, moved the lamp onto the table, and cast his eyes round the room. All was as we had seen it in the daytime. Then creeping up to me and making a trumpet of his hand, he whispered into my ear again so gently that it was all that I could do to distinguish the words:

"The least sound would be fatal to our plans."

I nodded to show that I had heard.

"We must sit without light. He would see it through the ventilator."

I nodded again.

"Do not go asleep; your very life may depend upon it. Have your pistol ready in case we should need it. I will sit on the side of the bed, and you in that chair."

I took out my revolver and laid it on the corner of the table.

Holmes had brought up a long thin cane, and this he placed upon the bed beside him. By it he laid the box of matches and the stump of a candle. Then he turned down the lamp, and we were left in darkness.

How shall I ever forget that dreadful vigil? I could not hear a sound, not even the drawing of a breath, and yet I knew that my companion sat open-eyed, within a few feet of me, in the same state of nervous tension in which I was myself. The shutters cut off the least ray of light, and we waited in absolute darkness. From outside came the occasional cry of a night-bird, and once at our very window a long drawn cat-like whine, which told us that the cheetah was indeed at liberty. Far away we could hear the deep tones of the parish clock, which boomed out every quarter of an hour. How long they seemed, those quarters! Twelve struck, and one and two and three, and still we sat waiting silently for whatever might befall.

Suddenly there was the momentary gleam of a light up in the direction of the ventilator, which vanished immediately, but was succeeded by a strong smell of burning oil and heated metal. Some one in the next room had lit a dark-lantern. I heard a gentle sound of movement, and then all was silent once more, though the smell grew stronger. For half an hour I sat with straining ears. Then suddenly another sound became audible—a very gentle, soothing sound, like that of a small jet of steam escaping continually from a kettle. The instant that we heard it, Holmes sprang from the bed, struck a match, and lashed furiously with his cane at the bell-pull.

"You see it, Watson?" he yelled. "You see it?"

But I saw nothing. At the moment when Holmes struck the light I heard a low, clear whistle, but the sudden glare flashing into my weary eyes made it impossible for me to tell what it was at which my friend lashed so savagely. I could, however, see that his face was deadly pale, and filled with horror and loathing.

He had ceased to strike, and was gazing up at the ventilator, when suddenly there broke from the silence of the night the most horrible cry to which I have ever listened. It swelled up louder and louder, a hoarse yell of pain and fear and anger all mingled in the one dreadful shriek. They say that away down in the village, and even in the distant parsonage, that cry raised the sleepers from their beds. It struck cold to our hearts, and I stood gazing at Holmes, and he at me, until the last echoes of it had died away into the silence from which it rose.

"What can it mean?" I gasped.

"It means that it is all over," Holmes answered. "And perhaps, after all, it is for the best. Take your pistol, and we will enter Dr. Roylott's room."

With a grave face he lit the lamp and led the way down the corridor. Twice he struck at the chamber door without any reply from within. Then he turned the handle and entered, I at his heels, with the cocked pistol in my hand.

It was a singular sight which met our eyes. On the table stood a dark-lantern with the shutter half open, throwing a brilliant beam of light upon the iron safe, the door of which was ajar. Beside this table, on the wooden chair, sat Dr. Grimesby Roylott, clad in a long gray dressing-gown, his bare ankles protruding beneath, and his feet thrust into red heelless Turkish slippers. Across his lap lay the short stock with the long lash which we had noticed during the day. His chin was cocked upward and his eyes were fixed in a dreadful, rigid stare at the corner of the ceiling. Round his brow he had a peculiar yellow band, with brownish speckles, which seemed to be bound tightly round his head. As we entered he made neither sound nor motion.

"The band! The speckled band!" whispered Holmes.

I took a step forward. In an instant his strange head-gear began to move, and there reared itself from among his hair the squat diamond-shaped head and puffed neck of a loathsome serpent.

"It is a swamp adder!" cried Holmes; "the deadliest snake in India. He has died within ten seconds of being bitten. Violence does, in truth, recoil upon the violent, and the schemer falls into the pit which he digs for another. Let us thrust this creature back into its den, and we can then remove Miss Stoner to some place of shelter, and let the county police know what has happened."

As he spoke he drew the dog-whip swiftly from the dead man's lap, and throwing the noose round the reptile's neck, he drew it from its horrid perch, and carrying it at arm's length, threw it into the iron safe, which he closed upon it.

Such are the true facts of the death of Dr. Grimesby Roylott, of Stoke Moran. It is not necessary that I should prolong a narrative which has already run to too great a length, by telling how we broke the sad news to the terrified girl, how we conveyed her by the morning train to the care of her good aunt at Harrow, of how the slow process of official inquiry came to the conclusion that the doctor met his fate while indiscreetly playing with a dangerous pet. The little which I had yet to learn of the case was told me by Sherlock Holmes as we travelled back next day.

"I had," said he, "come to an entirely erroneous conclusion, which shows, my dear Watson, how dangerous it always is to reason from insufficient data. The presence of the gypsies, and the use of the word 'band,' which was used by the poor girl, no doubt to explain the appearance which she had caught a hurried glimpse of by the light of her match, were sufficient to put me upon an entirely wrong scent. I can only claim the merit that I instantly reconsidered my position when, however, it became clear to me that whatever danger threatened an occupant of the room could not come either from the window or the door. My attention was speedily drawn, as I have already remarked to you, to this ventilator, and to the bell-rope which hung down to the bed. The discovery that this was a dummy, and that the bed was clamped to the floor, instantly gave rise to the suspicion that the rope was there as bridge for something passing through the hole, and coming to the bed. The idea of a snake instantly occurred to me, and when I coupled it with my knowledge that the doctor was furnished with a supply of creatures from India, I felt that I was probably on the right track. The idea of using a form of poison which could not possibly be discovered by any chemical test was just such a one as would occur to a clever and ruthless man who had had an Eastern training. The rapidity with which such a poison would take effect would also, from his point of view, be an advantage. It would be a sharp-eyed coroner, indeed, who could distinguish the two little dark punctures which would show where the poison fangs had done their work. Then I thought of the whistle. Of course he must recall the snake before the morning light revealed it to the victim. He had trained it, probably by the use of the milk which we saw, to return to him when summoned. He would put it through this ventilator at the hour that he thought best, with the certainty that it would crawl down the rope and land on the bed. It might or might not bite the occupant, perhaps she might escape every night for a week, but sooner or later she must fall a victim.

"I had come to these conclusions before ever I had entered his room. An inspection of his chair showed me that he had been in the habit of standing on it, which of course would be necessary in order that he should reach the ventilator. The sight of the safe, the saucer of milk, and the loop of whip-cord were enough to finally dispel any doubts which may have remained. The metallic clang heard by Miss Stoner was obviously caused by her step-father hastily closing the door of his safe upon its terrible occupant. Having once made up my mind, you know the steps which I took in order to put the matter to the proof. I heard the creature hiss, as I have no doubt that you did also, and I instantly lit the light and attacked it."

"With the result of driving it through the ventilator."

"And also with the result of causing it to turn upon its master at the other side. Some of the blows of my cane came home, and roused its snakish temper, so that it flew upon the first person it saw. In this way I am no doubt indirectly responsible for Dr. Grimesby Roylott's death, and I cannot say that it is likely to weigh very heavily upon my conscience."

TIMELINE

MEDIEVAL PERIOD:	**450-1485**	COLERIDGE:	1772-1834
OLD ENGLISH:	450-1066	SMYTH:	1779-1849
MIDDLE ENGLISH:	1066-1485	MARY SHELLEY:	1791-1851
DANTE:	1265-1321	PERCY SHELLEY:	1792-1822
(banished):	1302	*RIME of MARINER* (1)	1817
INFERNO:	1308-1320	*OZYMANDIAS*:	1818
CHAUCER:	1343-1400	*STUPENDOUS LEG*:	1818
ARTHUR vs GMStM:	c. 1400	*FRANKENSTEIN* (1):	1818
CHRISTINE DE PIZAN:	1364-1430	*FRANKENSTEIN* (2):	1831
JOAN OF ARC:	1412-1431	ANATOMY ACT:	1832
LE DITIE:	1429	*RIME of MARINER* (2)	1834
MALORY:	c. 1415-1471		
CAXTON:	1485	**VICTORIAN PERIOD:**	**1830-1900**
NINETY-FIVE THESES	1517	POE:	1809-1849
		RUE MORGUE:	1841
RENAISSANCE:	**1485-1666**	*MARIE ROGET*:	1842
SHAKESPEARE:	1564-1616	*PURLOINED*:	1844
HAMLET:	1600	"DETECTIVE"	1843
DESCARTES:	1596-1650		
MEDIT on 1st PHILO:	1641	**AGE OF REALISM:**	**1850-1915**
COFFEE!	1650	SUFFRAGE:	1865-1920s
		DOYLE:	1859-1930
RESTORATION:	1660-1700	*STUDY IN SCARLET*:	1887
ROYAL SOCIETY:	1660	WHITECHAPEL:	1888-1891+
CAVENDISH:	1623-1673	*SCANDAL*:	1891
BLAZING WORLD:	1666	*SPECKLED*:	1892
ENLIGHTENMENT:	**1687-1789**	**MODERNISM:**	**1915-1945**
VOLTAIRE:	1694-1778		
CANDIDE:	1759	**POST-MODERN:**	**1945-PRES**
AMERICAN REV:	1765-1783		
TEA PARTY:	1773	**THE FUTURE!**	
DECLARATION!:	1776		
FRENCH REV:	1789-1799		
LOUIS XVI / MARIE:	1793		
INDUSTRIAL REV:	1760-1840		
CASTLE OF OTRANTO:	1764		

GOTHIC PERIOD: **1765-1890**

ROMANTIC PERIOD: **1790-1850**
BLAKE: 1757-1827
M. HEAVEN & HELL: 1790-1793
TYGER: 1794

THE PENDULUM SWINGS!
GLOSSARY OF TERMS
(warning! spoilers ahead!)

AESTHETICISM: a formal arts movement growing out of the late Romantic Period (and in response to the staid Victorian Era), extreme AESTHETICISM declared art (including literature) to exist solely for the purpose of eliciting sensual pleasure: hence "art for art's sake!" DIDACTICISM, politics, and morality lessons need not apply. Although the movement really doesn't get rolling until the *fin de siècle* of the late 1800s, Samuel Taylor Coleridge's (1834) *Rime of the Ancient Mariner* evidences a number of AESTHETIC traits: awesome (and artful) depictions of nature, self-reflection upon artistic creation, and an apparent disregard for narrative or ALLEGORICAL structure.

ALLEGORY: [Greek: "to say something else"]; any narrative that lends itself to multiple interpretations beyond the literal level, but especially one that operates at multiple symbolic levels simultaneously; an ALLEGORY is a sort of "extended METAPHOR" relying upon a set of SYMBOLS that—when taken as a whole—suggest a secondary or tertiary way (political, historical, psychological, moral) of understanding the primary (literal) narrative. ALLEGORIES are often marked by oddly-named characters (Everyman, Sin, or Una) who act as PERSONIFICATIONS of abstract concepts rather than rounded entities. Dante's *Commedia* is a clear ALLEGORY (starting in a metaphoric wood and following a pilgrim on a his/our journey), even if it seems like everyone there has a specific (and uniquely Italian) name.

ALLITERATION: [Latin: "to the letter"]; the repetition of similarly valued consonant or vowel sounds in lines (or half lines) of poetry. ALLITERATION can be divided into *assonance* (the repetition of vowel phonemes) and *consonance* (the repetition of consonant phonemes). ALLITERATION was typical of Old English poems like "The Wanderer" and *Beowulf*, which were not end-rhymed, but metrically and phonemically balanced. ALLITERATION made a come-back during the Alliterative Revival of the later Middle Ages, as in *The Alliterative Morte Arthure*: "…foam flew from his face half a foot forth: // **Ph**legm so flecked his face and forehead, // It seemed freckled, like the flesh of a frog."

ANACHRONISM: [Greek: "against time"]; something temporally displaced or inappropriate to a particular time or place, like George Washington using a cell phone, or a Starbucks cup popping up in *Game of Thrones*. Perhaps the most infamous literary ANACHRONISM occurs in Shakespeare's *Julius Caesar*, when Brutus and Cassius note that "the clock has stricken three" (since chiming clocks were not a Classical Roman invention). Although ANACHRONISMS are typically thought of as authorial errors, they can be employed purposefully—and often comically; see, for example, the various intentional temporal mash-ups of *Monty Python and the Holy Grail* (the Holy Hand Grenade, the Marxist rants of the peasant Dennis, and so forth).

ANTHROPOMORPHIC: [Greek: "with human form"]; a type of PERSONIFICATION in which a non-human entity (flora, fauna, inanimate object, or abstract concept) is somehow endowed with aspects of the human form (arms, legs, a mouth) and typically human abilities (talking, thinking, emoting). Think Mickey Mouse, Chip and Mrs. Potts, or Almighty Zeus. ANTHROPOMORPHISM is the most concrete of PERSONIFICATIONS.

ANTHROPOMORPHIC DILEMMA: the unintentional sympathy elicited by an ANTHROPOMORPHIC character, regardless of how awful they behave. That is, any "humanized" entity in fiction—because they are "like us" in form and execution—will engender reader identification. Milton's Satan is the premier example of clear "bad guy" who—because he is portrayed as far more "human" than Jesus or God—ends up getting readers (like the Romantic poets, Blake and Byron) to root for him.

APOSTROPHE: [Greek: "turning aside"]; not just a punctuation mark! In DRAMA, an APOSTROPHE marks the moment when a character on stage speaks to an absent person or inanimate object. Hamlet's address to Yorick's skull is thus an APOSTROPHE in a double sense.

ARCHAISM: [Greek: "to imitate the ancients"]; the use of obviously outdated or obsolete terms or expressions in a literary work; often employed to arouse a sense of nostalgia or to place the narrative in a bygone age. Milton was terribly fond of ARCHAISM (both medieval and Classical), as were the Romantic poets who followed him in the early nineteenth century (note Coleridge's use of old-school "-eth" endings, for example).

ARTHURIANA: the stories—whether medieval or NEOMEDIEVAL—dealing with King Arthur, the Knights of the Round Table, and Camelot. Back in the Middle Ages, the oft EPIC heroic stories of King Arthur and company were thought of as "The Matter of Britain" (while the "Matter of France" dealt with tales of Charlemagne and the "Matter of Rome" starred Alexander the Great and Julius Caesar). ARTHURIANA includes not only the positive EPIC tales of Camelot, but also the SATIRIC, bawdy, and comic bits as well.

ASIDE: a dramatic convention in which an actor speaks their mind to the audience, rather than to other actors on stage. In COMEDY, such moments might intentionally "break the fourth wall" and comment METATHEATRICALLY on the play itself; in a TRAGEDY, an ASIDE generally offers the audience information that informs the character's actions or clarifies the plot. Shakespeare's Hamlet talks to himself quite a bit, really: he should probably seek professional help. Related to the APOSTROPHE and SOLILOQUY.

AUTHORIAL FALLACY: see INTENTIONAL FALLACY

BILDUNGSROMAN: [German: "education/formation novel"]; a literary work (technically a novel) tracing the education, development, and maturation of a "young" protagonist. Practically speaking, any "coming-of-age tale" found within a range of genres, from medieval ROMANCES (like Malory's *Morte D'Arthur*, which chronicles Arthur's rise from bastard child to right-wise king of all England) or EPICS (like *Inferno*, which traces Dante's trek toward his moral place in the universe) to modern YA fantasy (like *Harry Potter and the Developmental Challenge of the Semester*) can be considered BILDUNGSROMANS.

CHIVALRY: [Old French / Latin: "horseman"]; a late-medieval moral and behavioral code of conduct applied to warrior-class noblemen (knights) during peacetime: respecting women, protecting the weak, obeying authority—esp. one's king—and so on. At its best, CHIVALRY could become a way of channeling violent and sexual impulses for the greater good / God.

COGITO ERGO SUM: [Latin: "I think, therefore, I am."]; René Descartes' "aha!" moment following his snow-blind self-doubt driven exploration into the reality of reality: the one thing Descartes could be sure of—not history, other authorities, his own senses, nor even his belief in God—was that his thought-process existed: thus, to even think about whether he existed proved that he must exist! Although Descartes first expressed this realization in his native French ("je pense, donc je suis") the Latin phrase caught on in Europe and gave inspiration to a host of LUMIERES during the ENLIGHTENMENT…many of whom missed Descartes' main point (don't trust no one / nothing!).

COLONIALISM: the imperialistic practice of acquiring political (and subsequently social) control over another culture or country. The subjugation of other peoples (whether financially, religiously, or ideologically motivated) through the often violent establishment of colonies typically results in short-term gains for the colonizer and long-term resentment from the colonized. The British Empire (upon which "the sun never set") COLONIZED a goodly portion of the known world between the sixteenth and eighteenth centuries, including the Americas and India. The sense of ETHNOCENTRISM that fueled British COLONIALISM during this period was often reflected (positively and negatively) in the CARPE DIEM love poems of contemporary poets (as in Sidney's *Astrophil and Stella* and Donne's "Elegy 19: To His Mistress Going to Bed"). It also bubbles beneath the surface in many of Conan Doyle's Sherlock Holmes stories.

COMEDY: according to the Classical (Aristotelean) definition, any DRAMA in which the main character begins in a "low" position but ends in a "high" one; typically, the main character(s) begin the play powerless/confused/broke/single and end up empowered/enlightened/rich/married. As a modern genre of DRAMA, COMEDY (and its many subgenres, which include the rom-com, sit-com, SATIRE, PARODY, and farce) can be more broadly understood as any DRAMA which aims to amuse the viewer rather than trouble them overmuch.

CONTRAPASSO: [Latin: "opposite-suffering"; Italian: "counter-step"]; a term coined by Dante for—and employed repeatedly in—his *Inferno*, the exact meaning of CONTRAPASSO remains elusive, but suggests something beyond simply "the punishment fits the crime." In the most exquisite examples of *Inferno*, the punishment of the sinner is simultaneously a reflection of the sinner's sin and its opposite. Paolo and Francesca, for example, sin by committing adultery: in life, they lost control of their passions (lust) and chose to "smash" together inappropriately. And so, in Hell, they are flung about with abandon in a whirlwind of sinners who cannot control themselves: they are repeatedly smashed into other "bodies" in a mockery of their sin…unpleasantly and certainly without any sexual satisfaction. So, while CONTRAPAS-

SO is a form of POETIC JUSTICE, it is a bit more than, say, Arthur eviscerating and emasculating the Giant of Mont Saint Michel because the giant was a cannibal rapist.

DIDACTIC: [Greek: "good at teaching"]; a fair description of any text that seeks to teach a lesson, impart a moral, or justify a point of view; in the Middle Ages, such lessons tended to be overtly religious (as in the highly evangelical "Dream of the Rood" or *Inferno*). Since ALLEGORIES tend to have an underlying "message" of some sort, most can be considered DIDACTIC…regardless of whether the message is clearly stated (*Inferno*), complex and confusing (*Rime of the Ancient Mariner*), or culturally misappropriated (*Paradise Lost*).

DOOBY SCOOB: in a typical episode of *Scooby Doo*, seemingly supernatural mysteries are ultimately determined to be mundane: the ghost haunting the old amusement park is always, it seems, Old Man Withers in a Halloween mask. Ah, Rationalism! In a Dooby Scoob (patent pending), a seemingly mundane narrative is ultimately determined to have a supernatural (or at least exceedingly bizarre) cause: child psychologist Bruce Willis was a ghost the whole time…or a "large fulvous Ourang-Outang of the east Indian Islands" perpetrating a double homicide in Paris, for example. Television shows like the *X-Files* and *Dr. Who* are fond of debunking smug post-Enlightenment Rationalism in this way, although earlier Gothic authors like Poe and Austen (and later, Lovecraft) helped establish the trope well before the Mystery Machine first hit the road.

DRAMA: [Greek: "action"]; one of the three major genres (formal categories) of literature, DRAMA is traditionally written to be performed on stage by actors. Sub-genres include COMEDIES, and TRAGEDIES, morality plays, mystery plays, interludes, masques, rom-coms, sit-coms, and so forth. See also POETRY and PROSE. Fun fact: a DRAMA can be written in POETRY or PROSE (or both!).

DYSTOPIA: [Greek: "bad place"]; see UTOPIA.

EKPHRASIS: [Greek/Latin: "an out-telling"]; a literary recounting or description of a visual or plastic work of art. Percy Shelley and Horace Smyth both have a go at EKPHRASIS in their separate-but-equal Ozymandias poems, which point to the anxiety/interest that Romantics had for art as construct. A form of METALITERATURE, EKPHRASIS makes the reader explicitly aware of the existence of art as a form/

subject, and therefore of the literature they are currently reading as art as well. NB: EKPHRASIS is not exclusively a literary phenomenon, and can also be defined as any work of art that re-imagines or describes a work of art from a different medium (a painting of a sculpture, for example, or the film version of a book).

EPIC: a lengthy narrative verse form recounting the larger-than-life battles of a (super) hero who stands as an idealized representation of his (or, historically less often, her) culture; god/desses typically meddle in these grand affairs. Common conventions within an EPIC include an opening Invocation to the Muses, beginning IN MEDIAS RES, lengthy Catalogues (of ships, lineages, and booty), Arming of the Hero scenes, the intervention of Gods, and massive Fights. Oh, how they loved to fight, those EPIC heroes. Milton's conscious attempt at creating a Christian EPIC is modeled on Homer's Classical EPICS (*The Iliad* and *The Odyssey*); Dante's *Commedia* is a moral EPIC without all the heroic trappings.

EPISTOLARY: [Latin / French: "of letters"]; a literary narrative largely consisting of multiple sub-documents (snail-mail or e-mail correspondences, newspaper clippings, diary entries, telegrams, blogs, and so forth) rather than a single straight-forward first- or third-person narration. This sometimes disjointed presentation of materials—very often from more than one POINT OF VIEW—can lend suspense or ambiguity to a text and require the reader to fill in the blanks. As a result, the EPISTOLARY NOVEL grew popular among Horror and Suspense writers, including Mary Shelley and Bram Stoker (*Frankenstein* and *Dracula*, respectively). Fun(?) fact: The term was originally used in Middle English (and current Christian churches) to mean a book of epistles to be read during mass, such as Paul's Letter to the Romans.

ETHNOCENTRISM: the belief that one's own culture (nationality, religion, ethnicity, political view) is superior to all others. ETHNOCENTRISM often leads to XENOPHOBIA and/or COLONIALISM. Arthur in *The Alliterative Morte Arthure* is the poster-king of English Christian ETHNOCENTRISM.

FLYTING: [Old English: "quarrel"]; insult-based verbal sparring or one-upmanship; employed in literature as a way of establishing the pedigree of a hero before his first big physical conflict (first you boast, then you battle, then you get booty). FLYTING was rather popular in early hero-lit (*Beowulf*) and in ARTHURIANA. Such pre-game trash-talk is seen nowadays in "yo mamma" fights, epic rap battles, and any-time New York plays Boston.

FRANCOPHONE: [Greek / Latin: "sounds French"]; a description of literature incorporating French loan words or French pronunciation; typical of Middle English literature (including Chaucer) following the Norman Invasion of 1066. Not to be confused with *actual* French, as employed by Christine de Pizan.

GALVANISM: In the early Nineteenth Century, GALVANISM became a briefly popular biological science interested in the application of electrical current to living (or unliving!) tissue to stimulate muscle contractions or revitalization. Named for professor Luigi Galvani, who first ran electrical current through frog legs in 1792. The unlimited potential of GALVANISM to bring the dead to life (as postulated in *Frankenstein*) failed to pan out, but it did lead to life-saving defibrillators and myriad formaldehyde-laced high school Biology classes.

GERMANIC: [Latin: "of Germany"]; a description of literature incorporating German loan words or German pronunciation; typical of Old English literature (like *Beowulf*) which reflected a "native" culture influenced by Viking raids and colonization. Misappropriated nowadays by American neo-nazis who seem to model their German on Oktoberfest posters and old *Hogan's Heroes* reruns.

GESTALT: [German: "shape"]; a holistic approach to understanding the universe and the particular elements within it: often aligned with the adage, "the whole is more than the sum of its parts."

GRAIL: any plot device used to motivate characters into action or to advance the plot; importantly, once the GRAIL is achieved, it enacts real change upon the characters or plot (unlike a MACGUFFIN). Named for the legendary Holy Grail of medieval Arthurian legend (a chalice which, when found by the Knights of the Round Table, heals the king—and the kingdom—of impotence thanks to the magic of Christ), literary GRAILS range from solid objects (the One Ring in Tolkien's *The Lord of the Rings*) to persons (Sophie Neveu in *The Da Vinci Code*) to abstract constructs ("true love" in any modern rom-com). Once these GRAILS are found/employed, *things happen* (evil is destroyed; the "royal bloodline" is protected; the lonely hero/ine finds happiness). When a MACGUFFIN is found, nothing really changes: go home.

GREAT CHAIN OF BEING: the hierarchy of the entire universe, according to Christian belief at any given time. In the Middle Ages, the GREAT CHAIN OF BEING *typically* went something like this (in descending order of importance and awesomeness): God; angels; saints; the king; the pope; knights; clergy; laity; animals; plants; rocks; Satan. Until the High Middle Ages, this CHAIN was considered inviolable, even within sub-divisions; even radical social mobility was deemed against God's will. After the Bubonic Plague hit Christian Europe in the mid-1300s, however, the GREAT CHAIN comes under scrutiny, as social classes—and thus perhaps all classes within the larger hierarchy?—are questioned.

HYPOSTASIS: [Greek: "standing under / under-standing"]; the non-Euclidean mathematical/theological understanding that Jesus is both 100% god and 100% man simultaneously. Fun fact: This was not always the "official" Christian understanding of the incarnation; Christ's miraculous HYPOSTASIS was made Church doctrine in 1215 at the Fourth Lateran Council. Funner fact: werewolves are also HYPOSTATIC. You know: because of all the hair.

HUBRIS: [Greek: "overweening pride"]; the chief flaw of most tragic heroes; doing great deeds can lead to "excellence," but the ensuing reputation oft leads to an inflated ego (excessive pride in one's awesomeness) which leads to a feeling of invulnerability, which leads to errors in judgment, which leads to a reversal of fortune, and—if one is lucky—a final "oh shit!" moment of clarity (epiphany) before one dies: in other words, aristeia → arête → kleos → hubris → hamartia → peripeteia → anagnoresis → thanatos.

HUMOURS: in Hyppocratic medicine (and later medieval and Renaissance practice), the four HUMOURS were blood, phlegm, bile, and choler. A person with a balance of HUMOURS would be balanced and happy, but anyone with an excess of a particular HUMOUR would show particular moods: blood (sanguine) folks tended to be extroverted, cheerful, or overly sexual; phlegmatic folks were calm, cold, or apathetic; black bile (MELANCHOLIC) folks were sullen, depressed, or ill-tempered; and choleric folks were touchy, passionate, or irascible. An understanding of the four HUMOURS led to a rise in PHYSIOGNOMY…and leechings. Oh, the leechings.

IDEOLOGY: [French / Greek: "the science of ideas"]; the self-evident beliefs (or rationales) that inform the customs and behaviors of a given social group. The dominant IDEOLOGY of a culture may be imposed by those in positions of power or happily embraced by the *hoi polloi*. Literary works (which are written by members of—but not necessarily traditional members of—any given culture) may support or question a dominant IDEOLOGY. See also ZEITGEIST.

IN MEDIAS RES: [Latin: "in the middle of things"]; by starting a lengthy and important story say, nine years into a major conflict, the EPIC poet can establish the grandeur of the overall story while focusing on the "good parts" of the tale (like Achilles pouting in his tent... and his BILDUNGSROMAN). Beginning IN MEDIAS RES has been popular in "EPICS" from Homer to Milton to Lucas. Fun fact: Malory's *Morte D'Arthur*—which essentially begins with Arthur's birth and ends with his death (?)—employs a counter narrative strategy called "ab ovo" (literally "from the egg"), a soup-to-nuts narrative covering the "whole" story of his hero.

INTENTIONAL FALLACY: the mistaken (or at least over-extended) understanding that any text can be fully "unlocked" if a reader knows about the author's life or biography. Sometimes known as the AUTHORIAL FALLACY, as if knowing the author's intent—or conscious end-game—determines textual meaning. Such a critical lens can be exceptionally dangerous when applied to authors named Anonymous. However, political and historical ALLEGORIES rely upon the reader's knowledge of the author, and so require a limited form of INTENTIONAL FALLACY for reasonable interpretation. Mary Shelley's *Frankenstein*, for example, is a richer novel if we know a bit about the author's experiences with childbirth, but it still works as a story without that inside information.

IRONY: see ALANIS MORISSETTE

LUMIERE: [French: "lamp-light"]; self-proclaimed intellectual "enlighteners" of the later Eighteenth Century who came to embody the Age of Enlightenment in their progressive (logical rather than faith-based) philosophical, literary, or political movements. Also, that cute little singing candelabra from *Beauty and the Beast. Be...our...guest!*

MACGUFFIN: a modern coinage popularized by Alfred Hitchcock, a MACGUFFIN is any plot device used to motivate characters into action or to advance the plot, yet the object/idea pursued has no actual "value" to the characters even if achieved: it is thus an "empty"

GRAIL. The most famous example of a MACGUFFIN in literature is the EPONYMOUS Maltese Falcon, a reportedly priceless statue that motivates characters to betrayal and murder; yet the statue—upon recovery—proves to be a worthless fake. Other fictional MACGUF-FINS include the repeatedly hidden letter in "The Purloined Letter," the glowing briefcase in *Pulp Fiction*, and the alien Continuum Trans-functioner in *Dude, Where's My Car?* Fun fact: MACGUFFIN is var-iously spelled "McGuffin" or "Maguffin" as well, so good luck with your internet searches. Funner fact: Before the term MACGUFFIN be-came more-or-less standard, the word "weenie" was used to describe the same types of objects by turn-of-the-century actress Pearl White (famous for the *Perils of Pauline* film serial), so…good luck with your internet searches?

MEDIEVAL TIMES: not the same thing as the Middle Ages, the Medi-eval Period, or Medium Aevum. MEDIEVAL TIMES™ is a cheesy Renaissance-faire-esque "restaurant experience" during which fake knights fake joust while American tourists wearing paper crowns eat fake medieval food outside of a strip mall in Jersey. Using the phrase MEDIEVAL TIMES to describe the age of Chaucer or Beowulf will set your professor's teeth on edge; conscientious young scholars should avoid such usage, obvs.

MELANCHOLIA: [Greek: "black bile / sadness"]; although technically a medical term, MELANCHOLIA was employed by Renaissance au-thors (including Shakespeare and Webster) to loosely describe anyone with dark mood swings—from Hamlet's action-stultifying depressive indecision to the raging lycanthropic madness of Ferdinand in *The Duchess of Malfi*. MELANCHOLIA—as an excess of black bile—shows its roots in medieval HUMOUR theory: all humans have four basic temperamental liquids within them (blood, phlegm, bile, and cho-ler); any imbalance in these HUMOURS thus determined one's general mood. From the four HUMOURS arose PHYSIOGNOMY. *SCIENCE!*

METAPHOR: [Greek: "carry across"]; the comparison of two seemingly dissimilar ideas/objects via an often unstated common attribute (the "tertium comparationis," as Prof. McGonagall would say: the third part of any comparison). In literary studies, the METAPHOR is closely related to the SIMILE, but a METAPHOR does not use the markers "like" or "as" to make its comparison. Thus, "you are my sunshine" is a METAPHOR, while "my love is like a red, red rose" is a SIMILE.

META-THEATRE: moments of dramatic self-reflection, epitomized by "play-within-a-play" scenarios which cause audience members to consciously recognize the artifice of performance. Hamlet's hiring of a group of actors to enact *The Murder of Gonzago* before the murderous Claudius is perhaps the most famous META-THEATRICAL moment in English literature; thanks to verbal and visual cues, Shakespeare's audience is reminded that they are watching actors (performing the play *Hamlet*) watching actors (performing the play *The Mousetrap*). Good META-THEATRE temporarily fractures the suspension of disbelief established by immersive theatre by making the audience self-consciously aware of their theatrical experience. In COMEDY, which is typically less emotionally cathartic than TRAGEDY, playwrights can METATHEATRICALLY "break the fourth wall" for laughs.

NEO: [Greek: "new"]; in the *Matrix* series, Neo is made "new" through the knowledge imparted upon him by Morpheus (the Greek god of dreams) and a red pill, before—shocker!—he is revealed to be the "One." I bet he even listens to Brian Eno.

NEOMEDIEVALISM: the predilection of modern texts to romantically "repackage" the Medieval Period in fiction (and "historical fiction")— think Harry Potter, *Game of Thrones*, *The Lord of the Rings*, and even *Frankenstein*. Such NEOMEDIEVAL works inevitably color the ways that post-medievals (from the Renaissance onward) think about the "real" Middle Ages (full of magic, dragons, chivalry, and so forth).

NEOPLATONISM: a revived classical philosophy touting the idea that all creation emanated from "the one" or "the good" (subsequently interpreted by many as "the one god"). Within a Christian milieu, NEOPLATONISTS proposed that all humans—having emanated from God—were capable of god-like achievements. NEOPLATONISM thus encouraged RENAISSANCE HUMANISM. Marlowe's Faustus is the poster-child of extreme NEOPLATONISM ("A sound magician is a mighty god"), while the burden of decision-making that plagues Hamlet speaks to the anxiety arising from the realization that human actions are seldom godlike. Fun Fact: NEOPLATONISTS thought they were following in the footsteps of the great thinker, Plato; they were, in fact, following a pseudo-Plato: Plotinus.

ORDEAL: [OE: "judgment"]; in medieval practice/pseudo-history, an ORDEAL was a physical test enacted to determine ones guilt or innocence: a contrived moment where divine justice could be seen on

Earth. For example, a woman accused of adultery might be subjected to carrying a red-hot poker for ten paces, or walk blindfolded through ploughshares; if her wounds healed well enough after ten days, she would be judged innocent; if her wounds festered, she would be judged guilty. TRIAL BY COMBAT—wherein two knights would fight to see who was "right"—is a type of ORDEAL, and another orchestrated moment where God would be "invited" to reveal guilt or innocence. However you slice it, ORDEALS tended to justify a "might makes right" mentality.

PANOPTICON: [Greek: "all-seeing"]; technically, a type of prison in which a central warden could see—at all times—a "ring" of inmates without their knowledge (think a central lookout tower in a circle of cells). In a broader sense, a PANOPTICON describes any situation wherein the masses are under constant—and potentially invisible—observation by an authority figure. Such surveillance leads—in theory, at least—to self-corrective behavior based on the assumption that reward or punishment awaits those who behave or misbehave. Literary examples of such "invisible omnipresence" include Dante's *Inferno* (an omniscient God sees all), Shakespeare's *Hamlet* (Denmark is surveillance state full of spies), and Haven Gillespie and J. Frederick Coots' *Santa Claus is Coming to Town* ("He sees you when you're sleeping...").
NB: The prison system from which the idea derives came from Englishman Jeremy Bentham (c. 1800), a somewhat paranoid social reformer.

PARODY: [Greek: "mocking-song"]; although a sixteenth-century English coinage (Ben Jonson), the comic sub-genre has existed since well before the Middle Ages, and is one of the more obvious forms of METATHEATRICALITY on record. In PARODY, an author mocks or hyperbolizes an existing work, author, style, or genre in a comic fashion—thus inhabiting the mocked creation while simultaneously alerting readers to the silliness of its essential characteristics. *Bored of the Rings*, the *Scary Movie* franchise, and *The Colbert Report* are fine examples of PARODY (one mocks a single text; the other a genre, and the third a type of character). Compare to the more critical SATIRE, which comically hyperbolizes its target without necessarily inhabiting the target work. PARODY is closely related to burlesque, mock epic, travesty, and caricature.

PATHETIC FALLACY: [Greek: "emotional falsehood"]; a sub-category of PERSONIFICATION, a PATHETIC FALLACY attributes human feelings or emotions to non-human objects, often in response to narrative events or character moods. And so, when the weather turns foul and lightning strikes as Dr. Frankenstein creates his creature, nature reflects the "dark" mood of the narrative event and lends suitable atmosphere to the scene. Romantic poets—like Samuel Taylor Coleridge—were terribly fond of the device, since humanizing nature makes nature naturally supernatural. PATHETIC FALLACY is distinct from ANTHROPOMORPHISM, however; in both, non-human objects take on human attributes, but in PATHETIC FALLACY the attributes are restricted to figurative emotional response (the wind sighs; the sky weeps; the earth trembles), whereas in ANTHROPOMORPHISM, non-human objects literally take on physical human attributes (Mr. Tumnus speaks and plays the flute; Mickey Mouse whistles and wears pants; the giggling Teletubby sun has a creepy baby face). Although less common, the PATHETIC FALLACY can be employed (often METATHEATRICALLY) for comic purposes as well: see Eye-gore and Dr. Fronkensteen in the graveyard, for example: "Could be worse..." Fun Fact: although the term was first coined (by a Victorian) in contempt, a PATHETIC FALLACY is neither narratively "fallacious" nor necessarily "sad": common usage now understands the device as an intentional authorial choice without inherent bias.

PERSONIFICATION: [French/Latin: "to make a person"]; the attribution of human qualities and/or appearance to non-human objects, creatures, or abstract concepts. PERSONIFICATION can range from APOSTROPHE and PATHETIC FALLACY to PROSOPOPEIA and full-bore ANTHROPOMORPHISM. Granted, some critics see PERSONIFICATION as a lesser type of figurative language that most closely resembles PROSOPOPOEIA, but the old-school definition as a broad category remains terribly helpful.

PHYSIOGNOMY: [Greek: "judging via features"]; the medieval science of interpreting someone's inner morality from their outward appearance; a knowledge of the four HUMOURS (blood, phlegm, bile, and choler) is essential for an accurate reading, of course. Typical PHYSIOGNOMIC stereotyping would judge redheads as prone to anger or lust, and pale folk as being inherently dull or sullen. Nowadays, this sort of "judging a book by its cover" is considered (at best) "profiling" or (at worst) "racism."

POETIC JUSTICE: a literary device in which the good are rewarded and

the evil are punished, often with a side of IRONY. When Arthur evis-
cerates and emasculates the Giant of Mont Saint Michel because the giant was a cannibal rapist, that's POETIC JUSTICE: the punishment fits
the crime(s). POETIC JUSTICE rarely relies upon any judicial process,
but is often narratively—and immediately—satisfying because it ob-
viates the strictures of law. Such extra-judicial justice was a mainstay
of Sherlock Holmes stories; witness the death of Grimseby Roylott:
poisoned by the very swamp adder he used to kill his step-daughter!
CONTRAPASSO, "hoist on one's own petard," karma, and Fabliaux
Justice are all related to POETIC JUSTICE.

POETRY: [Greek: "a creation"]; one of the three major genres (formal categories) of literature, POETRY usually privileges form over context;
rhyme, meter, ALLITERATION, balance, even shape are often para-
mount in POETIC verse. Sub-genres include sonnets, EPICS, lyrics,
pastorals, limericks, haiku, and . See also DRAMA and PROSE.

POINT OF VIEW (POV): the perspective of the narrator (or narrators) in
any text, typically divided into three possibilities: First-person Limited;
Third-person Limited; and Third-person Omniscient ("all-knowing").
There is no Second-person POV possible (although one could argue
that First-person Omniscient is possible, if God is the narrator). EPIS-
TOLARY novels often employ multiple POVs.

PROSE:[Latin: "straightforward speech"]; one of the three major genres
(formal categories) of literature, PROSE privileges content or plot over
form, eschewing rhyme or meter for "clear-cut" exposition. Sub-genres
include short stories, novels, romances, essays, and newspaper reportage. See also DRAMA and POETRY.

PROSOPOPOEIA: [Greek: "to make another speak" or "to make a
mask"]; a sub-category of PERSONIFICATION in which an inanimate
object is (typically) given human speech and emotion, but is not further ANTHROPOMORPHIZED. Best example: the Rood in "Dream
of the Rood" (which talks, but does NOT have Mickey Mouse hands,
or big wax lips, or any other human features). Unlike the PATHET-
IC FALLACY, PROSOPOPOEIA is a "real"—not METAPHORIC—
PERSONIFICATION.

PSYCHOMACHIA: [Greek: "battle of the mind"]; the internal conflict of
a character, sometimes articulated via SOLILOQUY or depicted via

ALLEGORY. Hamlet is the poster child for PSYCHOMACHIA (although *The Reduced Shakespeare Company* do a fine job centering PSYCHOMACHIA upon Ophelia…maybe / maybe not).

RATIOCINATION: [Latin: "calculated"]; nowadays, RATIOCINATION is the process of using clear logic or reason to come to conclusions. However, for Poe (who coined the term), RATIOCINATION was a method of analysis that employed both logic and imagination, or—in the context of the mystery genre—both forensics and profiling. Poe's RATIOCINATOR extraordinaire—C. Auguste Dupin—is the immediate precursor to the fictional Sherlock Holmes and the real-world "detective" (a word that post-dates Poe's neologism).

REGICIDE: [Latin: "the killing of a king"]; as with any all-you-can-eat buffet, there are plenty of 'cides to choose (from infanticide and suicide to genocide and insecticide); none are particularly pleasant…but the REGICIDE of Charles I was an unprecedented political moment that upended the political—and in many ways, the religious—ideology in England at the time, thus giving rise to discussions of the King's Two Bodies (particular and political). Hamlet, of course, debates becoming a REGICIDE to avenge his father's REGICIDE (and becoming a patricide to avenge a patricide, and a…).

RENAISSANCE HUMANISM: a cultural ZEITGEIST evidenced by poetic self-assertion and a revived Classical conviction that "man is the measure of all things." RENAISSANCE HUMANISM extolled the potential capacity of humans, reason, and the value of a good Classical (philosophical) education; in other words, they valued the Humanities or Liberal Arts. HUMANISM is a short-hand, really, for a complicated series of cultural shifts following the theocentric medieval period; however, RENAISSANCE HUMANISTS were not godless heathens! Milton and Spenser, for example, are considered HUMANISTS. Then again, so was Kit Marlowe…

REVERDIE: [Old French: "a re-greening"]: this poetic trope / genre invokes a return to Spring, to life, and to happiness through the use of conventional images of growth, the changing of the seasons, and sexual innuendo. Troubadours and minstrels sang many a ditty extolling the return to "good times" via REVERDIE; the opening lines of the "General Prologue" of Chaucer's *The Canterbury Tales* offer a fine example, as do "In the Summertime" by Mungo Jerry and "Summertime" by DJ Jazzy Jeff & the Fresh Prince.

SATIRE: [Greek: "goat-tale"]; as a post-Classical genre, SATIRE criticizes stupidity, turpitude, or vice via humor, exaggeration, and IRONY. Typically, authors of SATIRE attempt to correct social ills by mocking perpetrators of injustice, corrupt societal constructs, or counter-productive communal attitudes. The most famous English literary SATIRE remains Swift's "A Modest Proposal," but modern political cartoons (and TV programs like *The Daily Show*) keep the torch burning...as does *Candide*. Although SATIRE is certainly related to PARODY, SATIRE is more sharply critical of its targets while PARODY more gently mocks with its tongue in cheek. SATIRE strives to elicit laughter...and then a sense of "oh, shit...that ain't right: let's go fix it!"

SCHADENFREUDE: [German: "harm-joy"]; the self-satisfaction (or pleasure) derived from someone else's pain, humiliation, or misfortune. SCHADENFREUDE ("shah-den-froy-duh") is a stark example of the "superiority theory of humor," which (broadly) posits that we laugh because we're not the one in trouble. So it's funny (to you) if someone else falls down on a banana peel (or drops a tray of glasses or pees themselves in class), but if you slip on a banana peel it's just plain embarrassing. *Avenue Q* (the weird puppet Broadway show) sang a fine NSFW tune offering a catchy definition and pithy examples of SHADENFREUDE called "Shadenfreude": look it up?

SCOOBY DOOB: (see DOOBY SCOOB)

SIMILE: [Latin: "like"]; the explicit comparison of two seemingly dissimilar ideas/objects, typically using the linking terms "like" or "as." In literary studies, the METAPHOR is closely related to the SIMILE, but a METAPHOR does not use explicit linking markers. Thus, "you are my sunshine" is a METAPHOR, while "my love is like a red, red rose" is a SIMILE. And yes: SIMILE is etymologically cognate with "similar" (but not with "smile").

SOLILOQUY: [Latin: "alone-speak"]; a dramatic convention in which a character "speaks to himself" at length on stage, thus offering the audience an insight into their thoughts via verbalized internal monologue. A SOLILOQUY oft reveals a PSYCHOMACHIA. Not to be confused with an APOSTROPHE (although akin to an ASIDE). Hamlet is a master SOLILOQUIZER; his "To be or not to be" speech (in particular) is often cited as a model of the form.

SONNET: a fourteen-line rhymed poem often (but not exclusively) devoted to matters of love. There are two chief SONNET styles: the Petrarchan (Italian) SONNET (abba/abba/cde/cde) and the Shakespearean (English) Sonnet (abab/cdcd/efef/gg). The Italian SONNET was popularized in England by Wyatt; the English SONNET was "invented" by Surrey, but is ultimately associated (as many popular Renaissance conventions were) to Shakespeare.

SYMBOL: [Greek: "thrown together"]; a term that, while holding literal meaning, also stands for something else, whether material or abstract; thus, within the proper contexts, "the bald eagle" stands for America, "Excalibur" represents Arthur's masculine prowess, and a "cigar" is, uhm, just a cigar. The *Inferno* starts off with a trio of walking symbols: the leopard, the lion, and the she-wolf; what they symbolize, particularly, may be debatable (lust, pride, and avarice, most like), but the important thing is that they are clearly *not* just three exotic wild animals strolling through an Italian forest. *The Fairie Queene*—and Spenser's unrelenting ALLEGORIES within—is so dense with SYMBOLS that somewhere, if you listen carefully, you can hear a green-eyed Dan Brown weep alligator tears of envy.

THANE: [Old English: "military follower"]; an Anglo-Saxon warrior, knight, or king's retainer; in the context of Germanic hero-lit (like *Beowulf*), a THANE was something like a "made man," really. King Arthur's knights are later (shinier and slightly less violent) medieval THANES. Fun fact: in his NEOMEDIEVAL *Lord of the Rings* trilogy, J.R.R. Tolkien named a thane "Thane" and a king "Theoden" (which literally means "king"). Man was a genius, is all I'm saying.

TRAGEDY: according to Classical (Aristotelean) definition, any DRAMA in which the main character begins in a "high" position but ends in a "low" one; typically, the main character(s) begin the play empowered/enlightened/rich/married and end up powerless/confused/broke/single...or dead. As a genre of DRAMA, TRAGEDY often elicits string emotion in an audience, and—through catharsis—helps to purge anxiety through a (happily temporary) vicarious identification with the doomed protagonist.

TRIAL BY COMBAT: (see ORDEAL)

UTOPIA: [Greek: "not-place" or "nowhere"]; coined by Thomas More to describe an ideal fictional island, "Utopia," in his satiric novel, *Utopia* (1516). As More notes, the coinage works two ways, really: "u-topia" is a fictional not-place, but it is also (homophonically) a "eu-topia" or "good place." It's the second definition that has stuck in the modern imagination, and gave rise to its opposite, the DYSTOPIA. Margaret Cavendish and Voltaire play with both ideas/locales: *The Blazing World* presents an intellectually UTOPIAN Blazing World (and limited but a not-quite-DYSTOPIAN Blinking World), while *Candide* features a violently DYSTOPIAN Europe and a peacefully UTOPIAN El Dorado. Attentive readers will note which worlds we live in.

VERNACULAR: [Latin: "native"]; also known as "common parlance" or the "vulgar tongue." A VERNACULAR is the everyday language employed by the unwashed masses (*hoi polloi*), rather than the elite (and sometimes "dead") language employed by those in entrenched positions of power. Once upon a time, English was not the most respected language in England: Latin was. Nowadays, Americans judge one another (aurally) according to perceived VERNACULAR dialects—New Yawkese, Southern drawl, Ebonics, and so forth—that are considered base variants of a "superior" form of English: British (or so my British friends tell me). Chaucer was a dab hand at bringing VERNACULAR English into literary prominence; so too was Mark Twain.

XENOPHOBIA: [Greek: "stranger fearing"]; the fear or hatred of aliens, foreigners, or "others." Oft accompanied by a strong sense of ETHNOCENTRISM, and employed to justify COLONIALISM. Although the term seems Ancient, it's a relatively new coinage (c. 1900). Still, the concept has been around since Homer, and doesn't seem to be going away anytime soon. >sigh<

ZEITGEIST: [German: "time spirit"]; a term typically translated as "the spirit of the age," a ZEITGEIST describes the overall IDEOLOGY of a culture: the distinguishing and unifying features / beliefs / attitudes / mood of a people. For example, the ZEITGEIST of medieval England might defined by a common belief in a Christian godhead, divine kingship, and the GREAT CHAIN OF BEING; the ZEITGEIST of modern America (USA) might focus on freedom, democracy, and opportunity…or not; it's not science, people!

This GLOSSARY [Latin: "collection of obsolete or foreign words"] was constructed from the living memory of the author (jogged into life by grad school lecture notes taken in classes under John Bugge and Jim Morey of Emory University) and with subsequent consultation to: *The Online Etymological Dictionary* (at www.etymonline.com); *A Glossary of Literary Terms* (ed. M.H. Abrams); *The Routledge Dictionary of Literary Terms*; *The Oxford Dictionary of Literary Terms*; *The Bedford Glossary of Critical and Literary Terms*; *The Norton Anthology of English Literature: The Major Authors*; and *The Devil's Dictionary* (by Ambrose Bierce).

Made in the USA
Middletown, DE
11 January 2020

82666254R00133